LINEAR SPACES OF
ANALYTIC FUNCTIONS

PASQUALE PORCELLI

Linear Spaces of Analytic Functions

RAND McNALLY & COMPANY
Chicago

RAND McNALLY MATHEMATICS SERIES

William LeVeque, *Advisory Editor*

Fine, AN INTRODUCTION TO MODERN MATHEMATICS

Gelfond and Linnik, ELEMENTARY METHODS IN
ANALYTIC NUMBER THEORY

Porcelli, LINEAR SPACES OF ANALYTIC FUNCTIONS

To Billie

PREFACE

THE CONTENTS of this monograph represent about one-third of the material the author presents in a first-year graduate course in complex variables. The course evolved (and continues to do so) over several years and has for its goals (1) a thorough grounding in analytic function theory, (2) the acquaintance of the student with the frontiers of knowledge in certain areas in analysis, and (3) the familiarization of the student with some of the literature, stressing both recent works and historical patterns. Involved with these goals are certain pedagogics which we won't discuss here but which may appear in various places within this monograph.

The selection of material presented has for its central theme approximation theory. Consequently, most of the theorems stated either lead to approximation theorems or are interesting results obtained from approximation theory. There are two reasons behind the selection of this theme. First, the author's continuing interest in such problems and, second, the fact that these problems are among the hardest in analysis and their solutions usually afford an excellent vantage point for a panoramic view of a great deal of mathematical analysis.

In the way of thanks, the author is pleased to express his appreciation to the administrators of Louisiana State University and Indiana University for making the aforementioned course and this monograph possible. Thanks are also due to the Office of Aerospace Research of the United States Air Force for their generous support of the author and his students. The author's colleagues, Professors George Springer, Maynard Thompson, Melvin Lieberstein, Pesi Masani, Frank Connor, and Sudhish Ghurye, were especially generous in discussing many aspects of this monograph with the author and are entitled to credit for its virtue but are free of responsibility for its faults. Also, in a personal vein, Professors H. S. Wall

vii

and T. H. Hildebrandt over the years have frequently discussed mathematics and much of the contents of this monograph with the author and it is a real pleasure for the author to acknowledge his indebtedness to them. Finally, it will be clear to the reader that the author has been greatly influenced by the writings of Professors A. Zygmund and E. Hille and the work of many gifted students.

PASQUALE PORCELLI

CONTENTS

Chapter 1

LOG MEAN

OUR PRINCIPAL GOAL in this chapter is to develop some of the standard theorems relating the growth of the modulus of an analytic function with the distribution of the zeros of the function and apply these theorems to the study of approximation problems on a variety of function spaces.

Throughout this monograph we shall assume that the reader is familiar with certain standard theorems from real and complex function theory, functional analysis, general topology, and algebra. In the way of complex function theory we assume that the reader's knowledge includes Cauchy's integral theorem and formula, elementary facts about power series, and the maximum modulus theorem.

Definition 1.0. Suppose R is an open subset of the complex plane and $\{f_n\}_{n=1}^{\infty}$ is a sequence of analytic functions defined on R. Then $\{f_n\}_{n=1}^{\infty}$ is said to be

(a) *bounded in compacta on* R if for each compact subset D of R there exists $M > 0$ such that $|f_n(z)| < M$ for $z \in D$ and $n = 1, 2, \ldots$, and

(b) *converge in compacta on* R if for each compact subset D of R, $\{f_n\}_{n=1}^{\infty}$ is uniformly convergent on D.

Theorem 1.0

If R is an open subset of the complex plane and $\{f_n\}_{n=1}^{\infty}$ is a sequence of analytic functions defined on R such that $\{f_n\}_{n=1}^{\infty}$ is bounded in compacta on R, then there exist a subsequence $\{f_{n_p}\}_{p=1}^{\infty}$ of $\{f_n\}_{n=1}^{\infty}$ and an analytic function f on R such that $\{f_{n_p}\}_{p=1}^{\infty}$ converges in compacta on R to f.

The proof of Theorem 1.0 follows readily from the Cauchy integral formula, separability of the plane, and the diagonalization process (cf. [92],

1

pp. 105–108, or [34]). Combining Theorem 1.0 with the classical identity theorem gives us

Corollary 1.0

If, in addition to the hypothesis of Theorem 1.0, R is simply connected, $z_p \in R$, $z_p \neq z_q$, $p,q = 1,2,\ldots$, $\lim_n f_n(z_p)$ exists for each p, and $\{z_p\}_{p=1}^{\infty}$ has a limit point in R, then $\{f_n\}$ converges in compacta on R.

Theorem 1.0 and Corollary 1.0 together are sometimes referred to as the *convergence continuation theorem*; this theorem has a distinguished history. An account of this history is given in [92], pp. 104–105. The results now form a special case of Montel's theory of normal families of functions [52].

Definition 1.1. Let $\{\alpha_p\}_{p=0}^{\infty}$ be a sequence of complex numbers. The statement that the infinite product $\Pi_{p=0}^{\infty} \alpha_p$ is convergent means that there exists a number $\sigma \neq 0$ such that for each $\varepsilon > 0$ there exists $N > 0$ such that if $n > N$, then $|\sigma - \Pi_{p=1}^{n} \alpha_p| < \varepsilon$. In all other cases the product is called *divergent*.

The following theorem exhibits relationships between certain infinite products and infinite series. We shall leave the proof of the theorem to the reader.

Theorem 1.1

Let $\{\alpha_p\}_{p=0}^{\infty}$ be a sequence of real numbers such that $0 < \alpha_p < 1$ for $p = 0,1,\ldots$. Then each of the infinite products $\Pi_{p=0}^{\infty}(1 - \alpha_p)$ and $\Pi_{p=0}^{\infty}(1+\alpha_p)$ is convergent if and only if the infinite series $\Sigma_{p=0}^{\infty} \alpha_p$ is convergent.

Theorem 1.2 (*Hurwitz* [39])

Let S be an open connected subset of the complex plane, $z_0 \in S$, $\{f_n\}_{n=1}^{\infty}$ a sequence of analytic functions which converge in compacta on S, f the limit function of $\{f_n\}_{n=1}^{\infty}$, and suppose $f(z_0) = 0$. Then either

(a) $f \equiv 0$, or

(b) for every circular region C about z_0, there exists $N > 0$ such that if $n > N$ then there exists $z_n \in C$ such that $f_n(z_n) = 0$.

Proof. Suppose C is a circular region in S containing z_0, $f(z) \neq 0$ for $z \in \bar{C} - \{z_0\}$, where $\bar{C}$ is the closure of C, and $\{n_p\}_{p=0}^{\infty}$ is an increasing sequence of positive integers such that $f_{n_p}(z) \neq 0$ for $z \in \bar{C}$. Then $\{f_{n_p}^{-1}\}_{p=0}^{\infty}$ ($f_{n_p}^{-1}$ is the multiplicative inverse of f_{n_p}) is a uniformly convergent sequence of analytic function on C and must, in fact, converge to f^{-1}, which contradicts $f(z_0) = 0$.

The following theorem and corollary form what is usually called the *Blaschke theorem* (cf. [3]) and is a fundamental tool in studying the behavior of an analytic function by the distribution of its zeros.

Theorem 1.3

Let $\{z_p\}_{p=0}^{\infty}$ be a sequence of complex numbers such that $0 < |z_p| < 1$ for $p = 0,1,\ldots$, and for each nonnegative integer n let

$$B_n(z) = \prod_{p=0}^{n} \frac{\bar{z}_p}{|z_p|} \frac{z_p - z}{1 - \bar{z}_p z}.$$

Then

(1) $|B_n(z)| < 1$ for $|z| < 1$ and $n = 0,1,\ldots$,

(2) $\lim_{|z| \to 1} |B_n(z)| = 1$ for $n = 0,1,\ldots$,

(3) there exists an analytic function B on $|z| < 1$ such that $\{B_n\}_{n=0}^{\infty}$ converges in compacta to B on $|z| < 1$, and

(4) $B \equiv 0$ if and only if the series $\Sigma_{p=0}^{\infty}(1 - |z_p|)$ is divergent.

Proof of (1) and (2). Suppose $0 \neq |a| < 1$ and $f(z) = (a-z)/(1 - \bar{a}z)$. Then $f(0) \neq 0$ and, for $z \neq 0$,

$$|f(z)| = \frac{1}{|z|} \left| \frac{a - z}{(1/z) - \bar{a}} \right|,$$

so that $\lim_{|z| \to 1} |f(z)| = 1$. Hence, by the *maximum modulus theorem*, $|f(z)| < 1$ for $|z| < 1$. Consequently, (1) and (2) hold for each of the factors of B_n and, therefore, for B_n. To prove (3) we note that, since $|B_n(z)| < 1$ for $|z| < 1$ and $n = 0,1,\ldots$, there exist an increasing sequence $\{n_p\}_{p=0}^{\infty}$ of nonnegative integers and an analytic function B such that $\{B_{n_p}\}_{p=0}^{\infty}$ converges in compacta to B on $|z| < 1$. If $\{m_p\}_{p=0}^{\infty}$ is an increasing sequence of positive integers and B_0 an analytic function such that $\{B_{m_p}\}_{p=0}^{\infty}$ converges in compacta to B_0 on $|z| < 1$, then the sequence $\{B_{m_p} - B_{n_p}\}_{p=0}^{\infty}$ converges in compacta to $B_0 - B$ on $|z| < 1$ for $|z| < 1$ and (assuming $m_p > n_p$)

$$B_{m_p}(z) - B_{n_p}(z) = B_{n_p}(z) \left\{ \prod_{j=n_p+1}^{m_p} \frac{\bar{z}_j}{|z_j|} \frac{z_j - z}{1 - \bar{z}_j z} - 1 \right\}.$$

Inasmuch as $B_0(0) - B(0) = 0$, we have, in accordance with Theorem 1.2, that either $B_0 \equiv B$ or the origin is a limit point of the numbers

$$[z_p; p = 0,1,\ldots].$$

In the latter case, we have from the classical identity theorem that $B_0 \equiv B \equiv 0$, so that in either case $B \equiv B_0$. This proves (3). For the proof of (4), we note that if $B \equiv 0$, then $B(0) = 0$, or, what is the same,

$$\prod_{p=0}^{\infty} |z_p| = \prod_{p=0}^{\infty} \{1 - (1 - |z_p|)\} = 0;$$

hence, by Theorem 1.1, the series $\Sigma_{p=0}^{\infty} (1 - |z_p|)$ is divergent. Conversely, if $\Sigma_{p=0}^{\infty} (1 - |z_p|)$ is divergent, then $B(0) = 0$ and, by Theorem 1.2, $B \equiv 0$ or the origin is a limit of the set $[z_p; p = 0,1,\ldots]$, which implies $B \equiv 0$, since $B(z_p) = 0$ for every p.

With regard to Theorem 1.2, the limit function B is usually called a *Blaschke product* and is denoted by

$$\prod_{p=0}^{\infty} \frac{\bar{z}_p}{|z_p|} \frac{z_p - z}{1 - \bar{z}_p z};$$

we shall use this convention throughout this book.[1] Also, the proof of (3) shows the essential role played by the multipliers $\bar{z}_p/|z_p|$ in each of the factors. Basically, these multipliers control the arguments of B_n at zero and, so to speak, keep them from rotating in a random manner.

Corollary 1.3

Suppose F is analytic and bounded on $|z| < 1$, $f \not\equiv 0$, and $\{z_p\}_{p \geq 0}$ is an enumeration of the zeros of f, each one being counted according to its multiplicity. Then the series $\Sigma_{p \geq 0} (1 - |z_p|)$ is convergent.

Proof. Suppose $\Sigma_{p \geq 0} (1 - |z_p|)$ is divergent. For each nonnegative integer n we set $h_n = f/B_n$, where B_n is defined as in Theorem 1.3. Each h_n is analytic on $|z| < 1$. Since $\lim_{|z| \to 1} |B_n(z)| = 1$, we have, by the maximum modulus theorem, that $\sup_{|z| < 1} |h_n(z)| = \sup_{|z| < 1} |f(z)|$. By the hypothesis on f, there exists $M > 0$ such that $|f(z)| \leq M$ for $|z| < 1$ and, hence, $|f(z)| = |h_n(z)B_n(z)| \leq M|B_n(z)|$. The divergence of $\Sigma_{p \geq 0} (1 - |z_p|)$ implies that $\{B_n\}_{n=0}^{\infty}$ convergences in compacta to zero on $|z| < 1$. Consequently, $f \equiv 0$, which contradicts our hypothesis on f.

Corollary 1.3 can be regarded as a generalization of the classical identity theorem. Loosely speaking, it asserts that if the zeros of a bounded analytic function f on $|z| < 1$ approach the boundary too slowly, then $f \equiv 0$. The condition $|f(z)| < M$ can be regarded as a "mean" or "growth condition," and

---

[1] We can allow for the, say, first n of the z_p to be zero. In this situation, the Blaschke product is of the form

$$z^n \prod_{p=n}^{\infty} \frac{\bar{z}_p}{|z_p|} \frac{z_p - z}{1 - \bar{z}_p z}.$$

one of the goals of this chapter is to find the "weakest mean" under which the conclusion of Corollary 1.3 holds. The mean in question is the log mean.

Theorem 1.4 (*Jensen's Theorem*)
If f is analytic on $|z| < 1$, $f(0) \neq 0$, and $0 < r < 1$, then

$$\log\left|\frac{f(0)r^n}{\Pi_{p=1}^n x_p}\right| = \frac{1}{2\pi} \int_0^{2\pi} \log|f(re^{i\theta})|\, d\theta, \tag{1.4a}$$

where $x_p, p = 1, \ldots, n$, denote the zeros of f in the closed region $|z| \leq r$ arranged according to ascending modulus, and multiple zeros are counted according to their multiplicity.

Proof. We first note, in the case where f has a zero on $|z| = r$, that the integral on the right side of (1.4a) should be regarded as an improper Riemann integral or as a Lebesgue integral. Also, we observe that when f has no zeros in $|z| \leq r$, (1.4a) is the Poisson formula. Our proof of (1.4a) rests on this observation. Suppose now that $r < r_0$ and that f has no zeros in the annulus $r < |z| < r_0$ and $r < \tau < r_0$. If we set

$$B_n(z) = \prod_{p=1}^n \left(\frac{x_p}{\tau} - \frac{z}{\tau}\right)\left(1 - \frac{\bar{x}_p}{\tau}\frac{z}{\tau}\right)^{-1},$$

$|z| < \tau$, and $h(z) = f(z)/B_n(z)$, then h is analytic and zero-free on $|z| < \tau$ and $h(0) = f(0)\tau^n/\Pi_{p=0}^n x_p$. If $r < r' < \tau$, then Poisson's formula gives us

$$\log|h(0)| = \frac{1}{2\pi}\int_0^{2\pi} \log|f(r'e^{i\theta})|\, d\theta - \frac{1}{2\pi}\int_0^{2\pi} \log|B_n(r'e^{i\theta})|\, d\theta.$$

Allowing $r' \to \tau$, we get upon using (2) of Theorem 1.3,

$$\log|h(0)| = \frac{1}{2\pi}\int_0^{2\pi} \log|f(\tau e^{i\theta})|\, d\theta.$$

Finally, allowing $\tau \to r$ gives us (1.4a).

The hypothesis in Theorem 1.4 that $f(0) \neq 0$ is not essential. In case f has a zero of order m at the origin, (1.4a) remains valid provided we change the left side to

$$\log\left|\frac{f^{(m)}(m)r^{m+n}}{m!\,\Pi_{p=1}^n x_p}\right|.$$

Also, (1.4a) has an extension to meromorphic functions and, in this direction, we refer the reader to [88], pp. 129–130.

We shall now define the "log mean" and develop some of its properties.

Theorem 1.5

Suppose f is analytic on $|z| < 1$, $f(0) \neq 0$, $r < 1$, and

$$L(f,r) = \frac{1}{2\pi} \int_0^{2\pi} \log|f(re^{i\theta})| \, d\theta. \qquad (1.5a)$$

Then

(1) $L(f,r) \leq L(f,r')$ for $r < r' < 1$, and

(2) $\lim_{r \to 1} L(f,r) < \infty$ if and only if the series $\Sigma_{p>0}(1 - |x_p|)$ is convergent, where $\{x_p\}_{p>0}$ is an enumeration of the zeros of $f(z)$ in $|z| < 1$, each counted according to its multiplicity.

Proof. If $r < r'$ and f has no zeros in $r < |z| \leq r'$, then $L(f,r) \leq L(f,r')$ where equality holds if and only if f is zero-free in $|z| \leq r'$. In the contrary situation, suppose $x_p, p = 1, \ldots, n$ denotes the zeros of $f(z)$ in $|z| \leq r$ and $x_p, p = n + 1, \ldots, m$ denotes the zeros of $f(z)$ in $r < |z| \leq r'$. Then

$$\prod_{p=1}^{n} \frac{r}{|x_p|} < \prod_{p=1}^{m} \frac{r'}{|x_p|}$$

and the left side of (1.4a) gives us $L(f,r) < L(f,r')$. To prove (2) we note that if $L(f,r) \leq M < \infty$ for all $r < 1$, then

$$\log \left| f(0) \prod_{p=1}^{n} \frac{r}{x_p} \right| \leq M.$$

Hence, if $r < r'$, then, arguing as we did above,

$$\log \left| f(0) \prod_{p=1}^{n} \frac{r}{x_p} \right| \leq \log \left| f(0) \prod_{p=1}^{n} \frac{r'}{x_p} \right| \leq L(f,r') \leq M.$$

Comparing the second and the fourth terms of this chain of inequalities and allowing $r' \to 1$, we obtain

$$\log \left| f(0) \prod_{p=1}^{n} \frac{1}{x_p} \right| \leq M.$$

Since this holds for every n, the infinite product $\Pi_{p>0}|x_p|$ is convergent so that, by Theorem 1.1, the series $\Sigma_{p>0}(1 - |x_p|)$ is convergent; then the left side of (1.4a) is bounded above and, consequently, $\lim_{r \to 1} L(f,r) < \infty$.

We define the "log mean" of an analytic function on $|z| < 1$ to be $\lim_{r \to 1} L(f,r)$ and shall denote it by $L(f,1)$.[1]

Corollary 1.5.1

If f is analytic on $|z| < 1$ and $f \not\equiv 0$, then $\lim_{r \to 1} L(f,r) < \infty$ if and only if $f = Be^g$, where B is the Blaschke product constructed from the zeros of f and g is analytic on $|z| < 1$.

Corollary 1.5.2

If f is analytic on $|z| < 1$ and $0 < r < 1$, then $-\infty < L(f,r)$ if and only if $f \not\equiv 0$.

The proofs of Corollaries 1.5.1 and 1.5.2 are left to the reader (cf. [60]).

We shall now investigate the distribution of zeros of the successive derivatives of bounded analytic functions. In general, the log mean of the successive derivatives blows up, and we are interested in the manner in which this occurs. In addition to their own intrinsic interest, these problems also arise in the study of fundamental sets of functions in a variety of function spaces.

Example 1.1. An example of a bounded analytic function f on $|x| < 1$ such that $L(f^{(p)},1) = \infty$ for $p = 1,2,\ldots$, is given by the lacunary series

$$\sum_{j=1}^{\infty} m_j^{-1} x^{m_j^2}$$

together with the sequence $\{r_j\}_{j=1}^{\infty}$, where the numbers r_j and the integers m_j are selected so that

(1) $r_j < r_{j+1} < 1$ and $\lim_j r_j = 1$,

(2) $\Sigma_{j=1}^{\infty} m_j^{-1} < \infty$,

(3) $m_s(m_s^2 - 1) \cdots (m_s^2 - p + 1)r_s^{m_s^2 - p} > \Sigma_{j=1}^{s-1} m_j(m_j^2 - 1) \cdots (m_j^2 - p + 1)$ for $s = 2,3,\ldots$, $p = 1,2,\ldots$, and we agree that if $p > m_k^2 + 1$, then $(m_k^2 - p + 1) = 0$, and

(4) $\Sigma_{j=s+1}^{\infty} m_j(m_j^2 - 1) \cdots (m_j^2 - p + 1)r_q^{m_j^2 - p} < 1$ for $q \leq s$, $s = 2,3,\ldots$, and $p = 1,2,\ldots$. For the function

$$f(x) = \sum_{j=1}^{\infty} m_j^{-1} x^{m_j^2}$$

---

[1] In all these results, we could eliminate the hypothesis $f(0) \neq 0$; however, with a view toward the applications we shall make of the log mean, this would be a little inconvenient.

and a fixed $p \geq 1$ we have $L(f^{(p)}, r_j) > m_j$ for $p < j$. Hence, from (1) of Theorem 1.5, $L(f^{(p)},1) = \infty$, $p = 1,2,\ldots$. In view of (2) of Theorem 1.5 and Theorem 1.1 we get that the infinite product

$$\prod_s |x_{sp}|^{n_{sp}}$$

is divergent, where for fixed $p \geq 1$, x_{sp} is a zero of $f^{(p)}$ of multiplicity n_{sp} and $x_{sp} \neq x_{tp}$ for $s \neq t$.

Example 1.2. In the above example it is not clear at this time if the divergence of the infinite product is due to $\lim_s \sup n_{sp} = \infty$ (p fixed) or if it can occur with $\sup_s n_{sp} < \infty$. We shall settle this by showing that the function f, constructed above, gives rise to uncountably many functions $\{g_c\}$ such that g_c is bounded and analytic on $|x| < 1$, (2) g_c' has no multiple zeros, and (3) $L(g_c',1) = \infty$. To this end, we define for each complex number c $g_c(x) = f(x) - cx$ so that $g_c' = f' - c$. If c and d are complex numbers such that $c \neq d$, each of x_c and x_d a complex number, $|x_c| < 1$, $|x_d| < 1$, and $g_c'(x_c) = g_d'(x_d) = 0$, then $x_c \neq x_d$ for $f'(x_c) = c$ and $f'(x_d) = d$. Hence, if D is an uncountable set of complex numbers such that x_c is a multiple zero of g_c' for each $c \in D$, then $\{x_c\}_{c \in D}$ is an uncountable subset of $|x| < 1$ and there exists $c_0 \in D$ such that x_{c_0} is a limit point of $\{x_c\}_{c \in D}$. Consequently, x_{c_0} is a limit point of zeros of f'' and, by the classical identity theorem, $f'' \equiv 0$, which is a contradiction because of the construction of f. This contradiction shows that, except at most for countably many numbers c, the zeros of $g_c'(x)$ are not multiple zeros and if these zeros are enumerated as $\{x_{ic}\}_{i=1}^{\infty}$, then the infinite series $\Sigma_{i=1}^{\infty} (1 - |x_{ic}|)$ is divergent inasmuch $L(g_c,1)$ is asymptotic to $L(f,1)$ by construction (cf. [67]).

We can say more about the zeros of the derivatives of bounded analytic functions. However, to do this we need to study certain types of analytic functions in the right half-plane and use a deep theorem due to Paley and Wiener (cf. [62] and [34]) which, in turn, depends heavily on the theory of the Fourier transform and, in particular, on the Plancherel theorem.

Definition 1.2. If f is analytic on $R_e z > 0$ and $1 \leq p < \infty$, then $f \in H_p(R_e z > 0)$ if

$$\sup_x \int_{-\infty}^{\infty} |f(x + iy)|^p \, dy < \infty.$$

$f \in H_\infty(R_e z > 0)$ if $\sup_z |f(z)| < \infty$.

Lemma 1.6.1

If $1 \le p < \infty$ and $f \in H_p(R_e z > 0)$, then (Cauchy's formula)

$$f(z) = \frac{1}{2\pi} \int_{-\infty}^{\infty} \frac{f(x+iy)}{z-x-iy} \, dy, \tag{1.6.1a}$$

where $z = u + iv$ and $0 < x < u$; moreover, (Poisson's formula)

$$f(u+iv) = \frac{u-x}{\pi} \int_{-\infty}^{\infty} \frac{f(x+iy)}{(u-x)^2 + (v-y)^2} \, dy. \tag{1.6.1b}$$

Finally, (1.6.1b) is valid in the case where $f \in H_\infty(R_e z > 0)$.

Proof. Consider the rectangle with vertices $x \pm iy'$ and $x' \pm iy'$, $y' > 0$, $x' > x$, and having z in its interior. By Cauchy's integral formula

$$f(z) = \frac{1}{2\pi} \int_{-y'}^{y'} \frac{f(x+iy)}{z-x-iy} \, dy + \frac{1}{2\pi i} \int_{x}^{x'} \frac{f(t-iy')}{t-iy'-z} \, dt$$

$$+ \frac{1}{2\pi} \int_{-y'}^{y'} \frac{f(x'+iy)}{x'+iy-z} \, dy - \frac{1}{2\pi i} \int_{x}^{x'} \frac{f(t+iy')}{t+iy'-z} \, dt. \tag{1.6.1c}$$

Suppose now that $z = u + iv$, z is fixed, and $T > |v|$. Integrating both sides of (1.6.1c) with respect to y' between $2T$ and $3T$ and dividing by T leaves the left side unchanged. For the second term of the right side we have

$$\left| \frac{1}{2\pi T} \int_{2T}^{3T} \int_{x}^{x'} \frac{f(t-iy')}{t-iy'-z} \, dt \, dy \right| \le \frac{1}{2\pi T} \int_{x}^{x'} \int_{2T}^{3T} \frac{|f(t-iy')|}{|t-iy'-z|} \, dy' \, dt.$$

Since $|t - iy' - z| \ge |y'| - |v| \ge 2T - T = T$, the last expression is dominated by

$$\frac{x'-x}{2\pi T^2} \left\{ \sup_t \int_{2T}^{3T} |f(t-iy')| \, dy' \right\}.$$

If $p = 1$, then

$$\int_{2T}^{3T} |f(t-iy')| \, dy' \le \int_{-\infty}^{\infty} |f(t-iy')| \, dy' \le M < \infty,$$

and if $p > 1$, then from Hölder's inequality,

$$\int_{2T}^{3T} |f(t-iy')| \, dy \le T^{1/q} \left\{ \int_{-\infty}^{\infty} |f(t-iy')|^p \, dy' \right\}^{1/p} \le M_p < \infty,$$

where $p^{-1} + q^{-1} = 1$. It follows, therefore, that the second term on the right side of (1.6.1c), upon integrating with respect to y' between T and $2T$, goes to zero as T goes to infinity.

The fourth integral on the right side of (1.6.1c) is handled in the same manner as the second integral. For the third integral we have

$$\int_{-y'}^{y'} \frac{|f(x' + iy)|}{|x' + iy - z|} \, dy \leq \frac{1}{|x' - u|} \int_{-\infty}^{\infty} |f(x' + iy)| \, dy \leq \frac{M}{|x' - u|}$$

in case $p = 1$ and

$$\int_{-y'}^{y} \frac{|f(x + iy')|}{|x' + iy - z|} \, dy$$

$$\leq \left\{ \int_{-y'}^{y'} |x' + iy - z|^{-q} \, dy \right\}^{1/q} \left\{ \int_{-\infty}^{\infty} |f(x' + iy)|^p \, dy \right\}^{1/p}$$

for $p > 1$. In either case the resulting expression can be made small by selecting x' large, and this can be done (the choice of x') independently of T.

To handle the first term of (1.6.1c), we note that for $1 \leq p < \infty$ and $\varepsilon > 0$ that we can select $y' > 0$ so that

$$\int_{-\infty}^{-y'} |f(x + iy)|^p \, dy + \int_{y'}^{\infty} |f(x + iy)|^p \, dy < \varepsilon.$$

Hence

$$\frac{1}{2\pi} \int_{2T}^{3T} \frac{1}{2\pi} \int_{-y'}^{y'} \frac{f(x + iy)}{z - x - iy} \, dy \, dy'$$

can be made as close as we want to

$$\frac{1}{2\pi} \int_{-\infty}^{\infty} \frac{f(x + iy)}{z - x - iy} \, dy.$$

Putting all these facts together establishes the validity of (1.6.1a).

In the case $1 \leq p < \infty$, (1.6.1b) follows from (1.6.1a) by setting $z' = -u + iv + 2x$ and substituting z' for z in (1.6.1a). Upon making this substitution, the resulting expression is zero inasmuch as z' lies outside the rectangle used in deriving (1.6.1a). If we subtract from (1.6.1a) the expression obtained by substituting z' for z we get (1.6.1b).

The case $p = \infty$ for (1.6.1b) follows from the case $p = 2$ by considering the function $f_\varepsilon(z) = (1 + \varepsilon z)^{-1} f(z)$, letting ε go to zero, and using the Lebesgue dominant convergence theorem.

This completes the proof of Lemma 1.6.1

Corollary 1.6.1.1
If $1 \leq p < \infty$, $f \in H_p(R_e z > 0)$, and $0 < x < u$, then

$$\int_{-\infty}^{\infty} |f(u + iy)|^p \, dy \leq \int_{-\infty}^{\infty} |f(x + iy)|^p \, dy.$$

Proof. Let P denote the expression

$$\frac{u - x}{\pi}[(u - x)^2 + (v - y)^2]^{-1}.$$

In accordance with (1.6.1b) we have (take $f \equiv 1$)

$$\int_{-\infty}^{\infty} P \, dy = 1 = \int_{-\infty}^{\infty} P \, dv.$$

Now if $p > 1$ and $p^{-1} + q^{-1} = 1$, we get from (1.6.1b),

$$\int_{-\infty}^{\infty} |f(u + iv)|^p \, dv \leq \int_{-\infty}^{\infty} \left\{ \int_{-\infty}^{\infty} P^{1/q} P^{1/p} |f(x + iy)| \, dy \right\}^p \, dv$$

$$\leq \int_{-\infty}^{\infty} \left\{ \int_{-\infty}^{\infty} P \, dy \right\}^{p/q} \left\{ \int_{-\infty}^{\infty} P |f(x + iy)|^p \, dy \right\} \, dv$$

$$= \int_{-\infty}^{\infty} \int_{-\infty}^{\infty} P |f(x + iy)|^p \, dy \, dv.$$

Interchanging the order of integration yields the desired result. The case $p = 1$ involves no more than the first and last step of the above calculation.

Let us recall that a Banach space **B** is a normed complete vector space over the real or complex scalar field. If the scalar field is complex, **B** is called a *complex Banach space*; and if the scalar field is real, **B** is called a *real Banach space*. We shall use the term *Banach space* to mean a complex Banach space. Under the usual notion of addition of functions and multiplication of a function by a complex scalar, each of the spaces $H_p(R_e z > 0)$ forms a vector space.

Corollary 1.6.1.2
If $1 \leq p < \infty$, $f \in H_p(R_e z > 0)$, and

$$\|f\|_p = \lim_{x \to 0^+} \left\{ \int_{-\infty}^{\infty} |f(x + iy)|^p \, dy \right\}^{1/p},$$

then $\| \cdot \|_p$ defines a norm on $H_p(R_e z > 0)$ under which $H_p(R_e z > 0)$ is a Banach space. $H_\infty(R_e z > 0)$ is a Banach where the norm $\| \cdot \|_\infty$ is defined by $\| f \|_\infty = \sup_z |f(z)|$.

The proofs of the above assertions are left to the reader.

Remark 1.0. Two of our immediate goals at this time are to, so to speak, set $x = 0$ in the expressions (1.6.1a) and (1.6.1b), and to investigate the distribution of zeros of functions in $H_p(R_e z > 0)$. These goals are obtained with the aid of the next lemma, which involves the use of functions of bounded variation. If $-\infty \le a < b \le \infty$ and φ is of bounded variation on $[a,b]$, then $\int_a^b d|\varphi|$ shall denote the total variation of φ on $[a,b]$. We shall always take our functions of bounded variation to be normalized; i.e., $\varphi(x) = 2^{-1}[\varphi(x^+) + \varphi(x^-)]$ for $a < x < b$. The basic result we need from the theory of functions of bounded variation and Stieltjes integration is the following: Suppose $M > 0$ and $\{\varphi_n\}_{n=1}^\infty$ is a sequence of functions of bounded variation on $[a,b]$ such that $\varphi_n(a) = 0$ and $\int_a^b d|\varphi_n| < M$ for $n = 1,2,\ldots$; then there exists an increasing sequence of integers $\{n_p\}_{p=1}^\infty$ and a function φ of bounded variation on $[a,b]$ such that $\int_a^b d|\varphi| \le M$ and $\varphi_{n_p}(x) \to \varphi(x)$ as $p \to \infty$ for each x in $[a,b]$; moreover, if $-\infty < a < b < \infty$, then

$$\lim_p \int_a^b f\, d\varphi_{n_p} = \int_a^b f\, d\varphi$$

for every continuous function f on $[a,b]$, and if $-\infty = a$ or $b = \infty$, then

$$\lim_p \int_a^b f\, d\varphi_{n_p} = \int_a^b f\, d\varphi$$

for every continuous function f on $[a,b]$ such that $|f(x)| \to 0$ as $|x| \to \infty$ and x in $[a,b]$.

Remark 1.1. The ideas involved above on functions of bounded variation were initiated by Stieltjes and extended by Hilbert (cf. [33], pp. 113–116) and F. Riesz (cf. [74], pp. 44–50).[1] At the present time, this result has been absorbed by a general theorem concerning weak star compactness of the dual space of a Banach space. Recall that if **B** is a Banach space, then the collection **B*** of all the bounded linear functions from **B** to the complex numbers is a Banach space, where for T in **B***,

$$\|T\| = \sup_f [|T(f)|; f \in B \text{ and } \|f\| = 1].$$

---

[1] These ideas are also referred to as the *Helly selection principle*.

B* is called the *dual* (or *adjoint, conjugate*) space of **B**. There are weaker topologies that can be put on **B*** and one of them is the so-called *weak star* (*w**) *topology*. A neighborhood for this topology is determined (at T_0) by $\varepsilon > 0$ and a finite set $f_1, \ldots, f_m$ of elements of **B** and consists of all T in **B*** satisfying $|T(f_j) - T_0(f_j)| < \varepsilon$, $j = 1, \ldots, m$. The generalization of the aforementioned result on functions of bounded variation is as follows: If **B** is a Banach space, $N > 0$ and $K \subset B^*$ such that $K = [T : \|T\| \leq N]$, then K is compact in the weak star topology of **B*** (cf. [35], p. 37). The connection between these two results goes back to the celebrated paper of F. Riesz [74], where it is proved that if **B** is the Banach space of continuous functions on a finite interval $[a,b]$, then **B*** is the space of normalized functions of bounded variation on $[a,b]$.

We shall leave the verification of the many assertions made in the last two paragraphs to the reader and return to our principal business.

Lemma 1.6.2

If $f \in H_1(R_e z > 0)$, then there exists a function φ of bounded variation on $(-\infty, \infty)$ such that

$$\int_{-\infty}^{\infty} d|\varphi| \leq \|f\|_1,$$

$$f(z) = \frac{1}{2\pi} \int_{-\infty}^{\infty} \frac{1}{z - iy} \, d\varphi(y), \tag{1.6.2a}$$

and, if $z = u + iv$,

$$f(u + iv) = \frac{1}{\pi} \int_{-\infty}^{\infty} \frac{u}{u^2 + (y - v)^2} \, d\varphi(y). \tag{1.6.2b}$$

Proof. Suppose $x_{n-1} > x_n$ and $x_n \to 0$ as $n \to \infty$. Set

$$\varphi_n(y) = \int_{-\infty}^{y} f(x_n + is) \, ds$$

and $\varphi_n(-\infty) = 0$. Hence, $\int_{-\infty}^{\infty} d|\varphi_n| \leq \|f\|_1$, and the result follows from our previous remarks together with (1.6.1a) and (1.6.1b).

Theorem 1.6.2

If $f \not\equiv 0$, $1 \leq p \leq \infty$, $f \in H_p(R_e z > 0)$, and $\{z_j\}_{j \geq 0}$ denotes the zeros of f each counted according to its multiplicity, then the series

$$\sum_j \left(1 - \left| \frac{1 - z_j}{1 + z_j} \right| \right)$$

is convergent.

Proof. Suppose first that $f \in H_1(R_e z > 0)$. If, in (1.6.2a) we write $\varphi = [\varphi_1 - \varphi_2] + i[\varphi_3 - \varphi_4]$, we find that $f = [f_1 - f_2] + i[f_3 - f_4]$, where each f_j has a positive real part. Setting $h_j = (1 - f_j)/(1 + f_j)$, we have H_j is a bounded analytic function $R_e z > 0$ and $f_j = (1 - h_j)/(1 + h_j)$. Hence, if $z = (1 - w)/(1 + w)$ and $K(w) = f[(1 - w)/(1 + w)]$, then K is analytic on $|w| < 1$ and is the quotient of two bounded functions, say K_1/K_2, and without loss of generality we can assume $K(0) \neq 0$. By Theorem 1.5, we have $\lim_{r \to 1} L(K,r) < \infty$, and (2) of Theorem 1.5 implies

$$\sum_j \left(1 - \left| \frac{1 - z_j}{1 + z_j} \right| \right)$$

is convergent. If $p > 1$, then the function $G(z) = (1 + z)^{-2} f(z)$ is in $H_1(R_e z > 0)$ and has the same zeros as $f(z)$.

We have the following corollary.

Corollary 1.6.2

If $1 \leq p \leq \infty$ and $f \in H_p(R_e z > 0)$, then $f = f_1/f_2$, where each of f_1 and f_2 is a bounded analytic function on $R_e z > 0$.

We shall return to the implications of this corollary in later chapters. For the present time, however, we shall exploit (1.6.2b) as a step in obtaining our earlier announced goal of setting $x = 0$ in (1.6.1a) and (1.6.1b). Our next lemma uses the fact that if φ is of bounded variation on $(-\infty,\infty)$, then $\varphi'(y)$ exists almost everywhere.

Lemma 1.6.3

If φ is of bounded variation on $(-\infty,\infty)$, $\int_{-\infty}^{\infty} d|\varphi| < \infty$, $z = u + iv$, $u > 0$, and

$$G(u + iv) = \int_{-\infty}^{\infty} \frac{u}{u^2 + (y - v)^2} \, d\varphi(y),$$

then $\lim_{u \to 0^+} G(u + iv)$ exists almost everywhere; in fact,

$$\lim_{u \to 0^+} G(u + iy_0) = \varphi'(y_0)\pi$$

whenever $\varphi'_1(y_0)$ exists.

Proof. If $\varphi = \varphi_1 + i\varphi_2$ and $\varphi'_1(y_0)$ exists, then

$$R_e G(u + iy_0) = \int_{-\infty}^{\infty} \frac{u}{u^2 + (y - y_0)^2} \, d\varphi_1(y)$$

and $\varphi_1(y) = \varphi_1(y_0) + \varphi'_1(y_0)(y - y_0) + h(y)(y - y_0)$, where $h(y_0) = 0$, h is continuous at y_0, and $\sup_y |h(y)| = \|h\|_\infty < \infty$. Consequently,

$$\int_{-\infty}^{y_0} \frac{u}{u^2 + (y - y_0)^2} \, d\varphi_1(y) = \varphi'_1(y_0) \int_{-\infty}^{y_0} \frac{u}{u^2 + (y - y_0)^2} \, dy$$

$$+ \int_{-\infty}^{y_0} \frac{u}{u^2 + (y - y_0)^2} \, d[(y - y)h(y)]$$

and

$$\int_{-\infty}^{y_0} \frac{u}{u^2 + (y - y_0)^2} \, dy = \frac{\pi}{2}.$$

Let $\varepsilon > 0$. Upon using the integration-by-parts formula, we obtain

$$\int_{-\infty}^{y_0} \frac{u}{u^2 + (y - y_0)^2} \, dh(y)(y - y_0) = \int_{-\infty}^{y_0} \frac{2h(y)(y - y_0)^2 u}{[u^2 + (y - y_0)^2]^2} \, dy$$

$$= \int_{-\infty}^{y_0 - \delta} \frac{2h(y)(y - y_0)^2 u}{[u^2 + (y - y_0)^2]^2} \, dy + \int_{y_0 - \delta}^{y_0} \frac{2h(y)(y - y_0)^2 u}{[u^2 + (y - y_0)^2]^2} \, dy$$

where $\delta > 0$ and is selected so that $|h(y)| < \varepsilon$ for $|y - y_0| < \delta$. Hence,

$$\int_{y_0 - \delta}^{y_0} \frac{2|h(y)|(y - y_0)^2 u}{[u^2 + (y - y_0)^2]^2} \, dy < \varepsilon \int_{y_0 - \delta}^{y_0} \frac{2(y - y_0)^2 u}{[u^2 + (y - y_0)^2]^2} \, dy$$

$$< \varepsilon \int_{-\infty}^{y_0} \frac{2(y - y_0)^2 u}{[u^2 + (y - y_0)^2]^2} \, dy = \varepsilon \frac{\pi}{2}.$$

Inasmuch as $\|h\|_\infty < \infty$ and $(y - y_0)^2 [u^2 + (y - y_0)^2]^{-2} < (y - y_0)^{-2}$, there exists $u_0 > 0$ such that for $u < u_0$,

$$\int_{-\infty}^{y_0 - \delta} \frac{2|h(y)|(y - y_0)^2 u}{[u^2 + (y - y_0)^2]^2} \, dy < \varepsilon.$$

Using the same type of argument for

$$\int_{y_0}^{\infty} \frac{u}{u^2 + (y - y_0)^2} \, d\varphi_1(y)$$

gives us $|R_eG(u + iy_0) - \pi\varphi'_1(y_0)| < 2\{\varepsilon(\pi/2) + \varepsilon\}$ for $u < u_0$. Arguing with $I_mG(u + iy_0)$ and $\varphi'_2(y_0)$ gives a similar result for $I_mG(u + iy_0)$.

Actually Lemma 1.6.3 is a variation of the Stieltjes inversion formula (cf. [92], p. 250). In fact we have proved the following: If

$$G(z) = \int_{-\infty}^{\infty} (z - iy)^{-1} \, d\varphi(y),$$

where φ is real-valued, then $R_eG(u + iv) \to \varphi'(v)$ a.e. as $u \to 0^+$. The expression

$$\int_{-\infty}^{\infty} (z - iy)^{-1} \, d\varphi(y)$$

is essentially the Hilbert-Stieltjes transform of φ.

Theorem 1.6.3

If $1 \leq p \leq \infty$ and $f \in H_p(R_ez > 0)$, then $\lim_{u \to 0^+} f(u + iv)$ exists almost everywhere, and if we denote this limit by $f(iv)$, then $f(iv) \in L_p(-\infty, \infty)$.

Proof. If $p = 1$, then the first part of the theorem follows from (1.6.2b) and Lemma 1.6.3. If $1 < p \leq \infty$, then we get the same result from the function $G(z) = (1 + z)^{-2}f(z)$ which is in $H_1(R_ez > 0)$. The last part of the theorem follows from Fatou's lemma.

The reader who needs to become more familiar with the classical theory of Lebesgue integration and the Lebesgue class L_p should consult [89].

Theorem 1.7

If $1 \leq p < \infty$ and $f \in H_p(R_ez > 0)$, then

$$f(z) = \frac{1}{2\pi} \int_{-\infty}^{\infty} \frac{f(iy)}{z - iy} \, dy, \tag{1.7a}$$

and if $1 \leq p \leq \infty$ and $z = u + iv$, then

$$f(z) = \frac{u}{\pi} \int_{-\infty}^{\infty} \frac{f(iy)}{u^2 + (v - y)^2} \, dy. \tag{1.7b}$$

Proof. We shall prove (1.7a) and proceed in cases. z is fixed in all cases.

Suppose $\varepsilon > 0$ and $1 < p < \infty$. There exists $y_0 > 0$ such that if $E = (-\infty,\infty) - [-y_0,y_0]$, then, for $p^{-1} + q^{-1} = 1$,

$$\int_E |z - x - iy|^{-1}|f(x + iy)|\, dy$$

$$\leq \left\{ \int_E |z - x - iy|^{-q}\, dy \right\}^{1/q} \left\{ \int_E |f(x + iy)|^p\, dy \right\}^{1/p}$$

$$\leq \left\{ \int_E |z - x - iy|^{-q}\, dy \right\}^{1/q} \left\{ \int_{-\infty}^{\infty} |f(x + iy)|^p\, dy \right\}^{1/p} < \frac{\varepsilon}{8}$$

and

$$\int_E |z - iy|^{-1}|f(iy)|\, dy < \frac{\varepsilon}{8}.$$

There exists $x_0 > 0$ such that if $0 < x < x_0$, then

$$\int_{-y_0}^{y_0} |(z - iy)^{-1} - (z - x - iy)^{-1}||f(x + iy)|\, dy < \varepsilon/8.$$

Using the Egoroff theorem (!) (cf. [89], p. 339) we have, for the same ε and $\delta = \varepsilon(8\|f\|_p)^{-1}$, that there exist $x_1 > 0$ and a subset D of $[-y_0,y_0]$ such that for $0 < x < x_1$,

$$|f(x + iy) - f(iy)| < \varepsilon\left(8 \int_{-y_0}^{y_0} |z - is|^{-1}\, ds \right)^{-1}$$

for $y \notin D$, and

$$\int_D |z - iy|^{-q}\, dy < \delta^q.$$

Putting all these inequalities together yields

$$\left| \int_{-\infty}^{\infty} (z - iy)^{-1}f(iy)\, dy - \int_{-\infty}^{\infty} (z - x - iy)^{-1}f(x + iy)\, dy \right| < \varepsilon.$$

Suppose $p = 1$. Arguing in the same manner as above, we can immediately reduce the problem to showing that

$$\int_{-y_0}^{y_0} (z - iy)^{-1}f(x + iy)\, dy \to \int_{-y_0}^{y_0} (z - iy)^{-1}f(iy)\, dy$$

as $x \to 0^+$. Suppose first that f is zero-free, so that $f^{1/2}$ is well defined and belongs to $H_2(R_e z > 0)$. Hence

$$\int_{-y_0}^{y_0} (z - iy)^{-1} |f(iy) - f(x + iy)| \, dy$$

$$= \int_{-y_0}^{y_0} |z - iy|^{-1} |f^{1/2}(iy) - f^{1/2}(x + iy)| \cdot |f^{1/2}(iy) + f^{1/2}(x + iy)| \, dy$$

and the result follows from Schwarz's inequality.

If f is not zero-free, then paraphrasing the construction used in Theorem 1.3 and recalling that $w = (1 - z)(1 + z)^{-1}$ is a conformal map betweem $|w| < 1$ and $R_e z > 0$ with inverse $z = (1 - w)(1 + w)^{-1}$, then $f = BH$, where

$$B_n(z) = \prod_{p=1}^{n} \frac{z_p - z}{\bar{z}_p + z} \frac{1 - \bar{z}_p}{1 + z_p} \left| \frac{1 + z_p}{1 - z_p} \right|,$$

$\{B_n\}_{n=0}^{\infty}$ converges in compacta to B on $R_e z > 0$, $|B_n(z)| < 1$, $|B_n(u + iv)| \to 1$ as $u \to 0^+$, and $\{z_p\}_{p \geq 0}$ is an enumeration of the zeros of f each counted according to its multiplicity. We shall show that H belongs to $H_1(R_e z > 0)$. To this end, we have for $\varepsilon > 0$ and sufficiently large n,

$$\int_{v_1}^{v_2} |H(u + iv)| \, dv = \int_{v_1}^{v_2} \left| \frac{f(u + iv)}{B(u + iv)} \right| \, dv \leq (1 + \varepsilon) \int_{v_1}^{v_2} \left| \frac{f(u + iv)}{B_n(u + iv)} \right| \, dv.$$

The function f/B_n belongs to $H_1(R_e z > 0)$ and, since $|B_n(u + iv)| \to 1$ as $u \to 0^+$, we get from Corollary 1.6.1.1 that

$$\int_{v_1}^{v_2} \left| \frac{f(u + iv)}{B_n(u + iv)} \right| \, dv \leq \lim_{u \to 0^+} \int_{v_1}^{v_2} |f(u + iv)| \, dv,$$

or $\|H\|_1 \leq \|f\|_1$ (in fact, $\|H\|_1 = \|f\|_1$). Hence

$$\int_{-\infty}^{\infty} |z - iy|^{-1} |f(x + iy) - f(x_1 + iy)| \, dy$$

$$\leq \int_{-\infty}^{\infty} |z - iy|^{-1} |B(x + iy)| \cdot |H(x + iy) - H(x_1 + iy)| \, dy$$

$$+ \int_{-\infty}^{\infty} |z - iy|^{-1} \cdot |H(x_1 + iy)| \cdot |B(x + iy) - B(x_1 + iy)| \, dy.$$

The zero-free case for $p = 1$ shows that the first of the above integrals on the right goes to zero with x and x_1. Since $B \in H_\infty(R_e z > 0)(\|B\|_\infty = 1)$,

Theorem 1.6.3 gives us that $\lim_{x \to 0^+} B(x + iy)$ exists almost everywhere; therefore,

$$\int_{-\infty}^{\infty} |z - iy|^{-1} \cdot |H(x + iy)| \cdot |B(x + iy) - B(x_1 + iy)|\, dy$$

$$\leq 2 \int_{-\infty}^{\infty} |z - iy|^{-1} \cdot |H(x + iy) - H(iy)|\, dy$$

$$+ 2 \int_{-\infty}^{\infty} |z - iy| \cdot |B(x + iy) - B(x_1 + iy)| \cdot |H(iy)|\, dy.$$

The first of the two last integrals goes to zero in view of the zero-free case and the second goes to zero by virtue of the Lebesgue dominant convergence theorem.

This completes the proof of (1.7a). The proof of (1.7b) is left to the reader. As a consequence of our argument we also have that

$$\int_{-\infty}^{\infty} |f(iy) - f(x + iy)|^p\, dy \to 0$$

as $x \to 0^+$.

Before using the preceding theorems to establish the Paley–Wiener theorem, we shall state some needed facts from the theory of the Fourier transform; in particular, Plancherel's theorem. This theorem tells us that if $f \in L_2(-\infty,\infty)$, $a > 0$ and

$$\hat{f}(t) = \frac{1}{\sqrt{2\pi}} \lim_{a \to \infty} \int_{-a}^{a} e^{-ist} f(s)\, ds,$$

then $\hat{f} \in L_2(-\infty,\infty)$ and

$$\int_{-\infty}^{\infty} |\hat{f}(t)|^2\, dt = \int_{-\infty}^{\infty} |f(s)|^2\, ds.$$

Moreover,

$$f(t) = \frac{1}{\sqrt{2\pi}} \lim_{a \to \infty} \int_{-a}^{a} e^{ist} \hat{f}(s)\, ds.$$

Plancherel's theorem implies Parseval's theorem, which asserts that if f and h belong to $L_2(-\infty,\infty)$, then

$$\int_{-\infty}^{\infty} f(t)\overline{h(t)}\, dt = \int_{-\infty}^{\infty} \hat{f}(s)\overline{\hat{h}(s)}\, ds.$$

We shall discuss these theorems further in Appendix A.

Theorem 1.8 (*Paley–Wiener:* cf. [62], p. 8)

If f is analytic on $R_e z > 0$, then $f \in H_2(R_e z > 0)$ if and only if there exists uniquely $F \in L_2(0,\infty)$ such that

$$f(z) = \int_0^\infty e^{-zt} F(t)\, dt. \tag{1.8a}$$

Proof. Suppose $F \in L_2(0,\infty)$ and f is defined in accordance with (1.8a). Then f is analytic on $R_e z > 0$ and, by Plancherel's theorem,

$$\int_{-\infty}^\infty |f(u + iv)|^2\, dv = 2\pi \int_{-\infty}^\infty e^{-2ut}|F_1(t)|^2\, dt \leq 2\pi \int_0^\infty |F(t)|^2\, dt,$$

where $F_1(t) = F(t)$ or 0 according as to $t \geq 0$ or $t < 0$. Consequently, $f \in H_2(R_e z > 0)$. Suppose now that $f \in H_2(R_e > 0)$. Theorem 1.7 gives us

$$f(z) = \int_{-\infty}^\infty \frac{1}{z - iy} f(iy)\, dy.$$

Since $f(iy) \in L_2(-\infty,\infty)$, there exists $F \in L_2(-\infty,\infty)$ such that $\hat{f}(iy) = F(y)$. The function $(z - iy)^{-1}$ is the Fourier transform of the function $g(t) = \sqrt{2\pi} e^{-zt}$ or 0, according as to whether $t \geq 0$ or $t < 0$. Hence Parseval's theorem gives us

$$\int_{-\infty}^\infty \frac{1}{z - iy} f(iy)\, dy = \int_{-\infty}^\infty g(t)F(t)\, dt = \sqrt{2\pi} \int_0^\infty e^{-zt} F(t)\, dt.$$

To apply the Paley–Wiener theorem to approximation problems involving the successive derivatives of bounded analytic functions, we shall need the following lemma due to G. H. Hardy (cf. [24]).

Lemma 1.9

If $F \in L_2(0,\infty)$ and $G(s) = s^{-1} \int_0^s F(t)\, dt$ for $s > 0$, then $G \in L_2(0,\infty)$ and

$$\left\{ \int_0^\infty |G(s)|^2\, ds \right\}^{1/2} \leq 2 \left\{ \int_0^\infty |F(t)|^2\, dt \right\}^{1/2}.$$

Theorem 1.9

If g is analytic on $|x| < 1$, $M > 0$ such that $|g(x)| < M$ for $|x| < 1$, and p a nonnegative integer, then the pth derivative of g is given by the formula

$$g^{(p)}(x) = 2^p (1 + x)^{-(2p+1)} \int_0^\infty e^{-zt} t^p K_p(t)\, dt \tag{1.9a}$$

where $R_e z > 0$, $x = (1 - z)(1 + z)^{-1}$, and $K_p \in L_2(0,\infty)$; moreover, the functions K_p are uniquely determined by g and p and are related by the formula

$$K_{p+1}(t) = K_p(t) - (2p + 1)t^{-(p+1)}\int_0^t e^{-s}(t - s)^p K_p(t - s)\, ds. \qquad (1.9b)$$

Proof. Let $f(z) = (1 + x)g(x)$ and $z = u + iv$. Hence, for all $u \in (0,\infty)$, we have

$$\int_{-\infty}^{\infty} |f(u + iv)|^2\, dv \leq M\pi,$$

so that by the Paley–Wiener theorem we get

$$g(x) = (1 + x)^{-1}\int_0^{\infty} e^{-zt}K_0(t)\, dt,$$

which is (1.9a) for the case $p = 0$. Let us assume, therefore, that (1.9a) is valid for $p = n \geq 0$. Upon differentiating the resulting expression we obtain

$$g^{(n+1)}(x) = 2^{(n+2)}(1 + x)^{-(2n+3)}\left\{\int_0^{\infty} e^{-zt}t^{n+1}K_n(t)\, dt\right.$$

$$\left. -2^{-1}(1 + x)\int_0^{\infty} e^{-zt}K^*(t)t^n\, dt\right\} \qquad (1.9c)$$

where $K^*(t) = (2n + 1)K_n(t)$. Since $(1 + x) = 2(1 + z)^{-1}$ and

$$(1 + z)^{-1} = \int_0^{\infty} e^{-zt}e^{-t}\, dt,$$

we have, from the convolution theorem of the Laplace transform, that

$$(1 + z)^{-1}\int_0^{\infty} e^{-zt}t^n K^*(t)\, dt = \int_0^{\infty} e^{-zt}G(t)\, dt,$$

where

$$G(t) = \int_0^t e^{-s}(t - s)^n K^*(t - s)\, ds.$$

Also,

$$|t^{-(n+1)}G(t)| \leq t^{-1}\int_0^t e^{-s}|K^*(t - s)|\, ds = t^{-1}\int_0^t e^{-(t-s)}|K^*(s)|\, ds$$

$$\leq t^{-1}\int_0^t |K^*(s)|\, ds$$

so that, by Lemma 1.9, the function $t^{-(n+1)}G(t)$ is in $L_2(0,\infty)$. Finally, if we set $K_{n+1}(t) = K_n(t) - t^{-(n+1)}G(t)$, then we get (1.9a) for the case $p = n + 1$. The proof now follows readily by mathematical induction (cf. [67]).

The preceding theorem allows us to elaborate on Examples 1.1 and 1.2. Even though $L(f^{(p)},1) = \infty$, $p = 1,2,\ldots$, (f a function from Examples 1.1 and 1.2), we shall show that if we restrict ourselves to the zeros of $f^{(p)}$ that lie in a region R where, so to speak, R has zero contact with the circle $|x| = 1$, then the Blaschke product (or series) of these zeros must be convergent (cf. [67] and [29]).

Theorem 1.10

Let g be analytic and uniformly bounded on $|x| < 1, 0 < |y_0| < 1$, C denote the circular region $|x - y_0| < |y_0 - e^{i \arg y_0}|$, and p a nonnegative integer. Then either $g^{(p)}(x) \equiv 0$ or $\Pi_s |x_s|^{n_s}$ converges, where the product is taken over all the zeros of $g^{(p)}$ in C, and for each such zero x_s, n_s denotes its multiplicity.

Proof. Suppose $g^{(p)} \not\equiv 0$. By a simple rotation we need only consider the case where $\arg y_0 = -\pi$. By (1.9a),

$$g^{(p)}(x) = 2^p(1 + x)^{-(2p+1)} \int_0^\infty e^{-zt}t^p K_p(t)\, dt.$$

There exists $a > 0$ such that the region C maps onto $R_e z > a$ under the mapping $z = (1 - x)/(1 + x)$. Hence, for $x \in C$,

$$g^{(p)}(x) = 2^p(1 + x)^{-(2p+1)} \int_0^\infty e^{-wt}H(t)\, dt,$$

where $w = z - a$, $H(t) = e^{-at}t^p K_p(t) \in L_2(0,\infty)$, and $R_e w > 0$. The result follows from Theorem 1.6.2.

Remark 1.2. Now we turn our attention to the problem of characterizing sets of functions which are fundamental in certain function spaces. Recall that if **B** is a Banach space and **K** is a subset of **B**, then **K** is fundamental if and only if no proper subspace of **B** contains **K**. That is to say, every element of **B** can be approximated (in the norm of **B**) by a linear combination of elements of **K**. A basic result in the theory of Banach spaces asserts that a necessary and sufficient condition in order that **K** be fundamental in **B** is that if $T \in$ **B*** (dual space of **B**) and **K** is in the kernel of T [i.e., **K** $\subset T^{-1}(0)$], then **B** is the kernel of T; in other words, if $T(f) = 0$ for every $f \in K$, then $T = 0$ (cf. [2], p. 58). We shall use this basic result in the next few theorems and corollaries in the case where $\mathbf{B} = L_2(a,b)$, $-\infty \leq a < b \leq \infty$. In this case $\mathbf{B}^* = L_2(a,b)$, inasmuch as for $T \in B^*$ there exists uniquely $f \in L_2(a,b)$ such that $\|T\| = \|f\|_2$ and

$$T(h) = \int_a^b h(t)\overline{f(t)}\,dt \tag{A}$$

for every $h \in L_2(a,b)$. More generally, if $1 < p < \infty$, then $L_p^*(a,b) = L_q(a,b)$, where $p^{-1} + q^{-1} = 1$, and (A) is valid with $h \in L_p(a,b)$ and $f \in L_q(a,b)$ (cf. [20], p. 286). Because of the structure of the real line, $L_1^*(a,b) = L_\infty(a,b)$ and (A) is valid (cf. [20], p. 289). $L_\infty^*(a,b)$ is much more complicated (cf. [20], p. 296; [19]; or [64]). An interesting account of the history and literature of these spaces is given on p. 387 of [20].

Theorem 1.11

If $R_e z_j > 0$, $j = 1,2,\ldots$, and $z_i \neq z_j$ for $i \neq j$, then $\{e^{-z_j t}\}_{j=1}^\infty$ is fundamental in $L_2(0,\infty)$ if and only if the infinite series

$$\sum_{j=1}^\infty \left(1 - \left|\frac{1-z_j}{1+z_j}\right|\right) \tag{1.11a}$$

is divergent.

Proof. Suppose (1.11a) is divergent and that $\{e^{-z_j t}\}_{j=1}^\infty$ is not fundamental in $L_2(0,\infty)$. Then there exists $F \in L_2(0,\infty)$ such that

$$\int_0^\infty e^{-z_j t} F(t)\,dt = 0$$

for $j = 1,2,\ldots$. In view of Theorem 1.8, this contradicts Theorem 1.6.2. Suppose (1.11a) is convergent, $x_j = (1 - z_j)(1 + z_j)^{-1}$, and B is the Blaschke function constructed with zeros $\{x_j\}_j$ in accordance with Theorem 1.3. From Theorem 1.9 we get

$$B(x) = (1 + x)^{-1} \int_0^\infty e^{-zt} K(t)\,dt$$

with $K \in L_2(0,\infty)$. $B(x_j) = 0$ implies

$$\int_0^\infty e^{-z_j t} K(t)\,dt = 0$$

which, in turn, implies that $\{e^{-z_j t}\}_{j=1}^\infty$ is not fundamental in $L_2(0,\infty)$.

Combining Theorem 1.11 with Example 1.2 and Theorem 1.9 gives us

Theorem 1.12

For each positive integer n, there exists a set of distinct numbers z_j, $j = 1,2,\ldots$, such that $R_e z_j > 0$, $\{e^{-z_j t}\}_{j=1}^{\infty}$ is fundamental in $L_2(0,\infty)$, and $\{e^{-z_j t}t^n\}_{j=1}^{\infty}$ is not fundamental in $L_2(0,\infty)$.

In view of Theorem 1.10 we have

Theorem 1.13

If $\delta > 0$, $\{z_j\}_{j=1}^{\infty}$ a set of distinct numbers such that $R_e z_j > \delta$, and n a nonnegative integer, then $\{e^{-z_j t}t^n\}_{j=1}^{\infty}$ is fundamental in $L_2(0,\infty)$ if and only if the infinite series (1.11a) is divergent.

The transformation $f(t) \to f(-\ln \tau)\tau^{1/2}$ is an isometric mapping of $L_2(0,\infty)$ onto $L_2(0,1)$. Consequently, the property of a set being fundamental is invariant of this transformation. It follows, therefore, that $\{e^{-z_j t}t^n\}_{j=0}^{\infty}$ is fundamental in $L_2(0,\infty)$ if and only if $\{\tau^{w_j}(\ln \tau)^n\}_{j=1}^{\infty}$ is fundamental in $L_2(0,1)$ where $w_j = z_j - \frac{1}{2}$. As corollaries to the last three theorems we have (using $w_j = z_j - \frac{1}{2}$).

Corollary 1.13.1

If $\{w_j\}_{j=1}^{\infty}$ is a set of distinct numbers and $R_e w_j > -\frac{1}{2}$, then $\{\tau^{w_j}\}_{j=1}^{\infty}$ is fundamental in $L_2(0,1)$ if and only if the infinite series

$$\sum_{j=1}^{\infty}\left(1 - \left|\frac{1 - 2w_j}{3 + 2w_j}\right|\right) \qquad (1.13a)$$

is divergent.

Corollary 1.13.2

For each nonnegative integer n, there exists a set of distinct numbers w_j such that $R_e w_j > -\frac{1}{2}$, $\{\tau^{w_j}\}_{j=1}^{\infty}$ is fundamental in $L_2(0,1)$, and $\{\tau^{w_j}(\ln \tau)^n\}_{j=1}^{\infty}$ is not fundamental in $L_2(0,1)$.

Corollary 1.13.3

If $\delta > -\frac{1}{2}$, $\{w_j\}_{j=1}^{\infty}$ a set of distinct numbers such that $R_e w_j > \delta$, and n a nonnegative integer, then $\{\tau^{w_j}(\ln \tau)^n\}_{j=1}^{\infty}$ is fundamental in $L_2(0,1)$ if and only if the infinite series (1.13a) is divergent.

The last three theorems and corollaries come from [63], [57], [86], and [67].

We shall now give a heuristic explanation of what is involved in the differences between, say, Theorems 1.12 and 1.13. To do this we use a representation theorem for the derivatives of functions in $H_2(R_e z > 0)$ (cf. [68]). If n is a nonnegative integer, then R_n will denote the positive cone in the $(2n + 1)$-dimensional Euclidean space; i.e., $(t_1, \ldots, t_{2n+1}) \in R_n$ if and only if $t_j \geq 0$, $j = 1, 2, \ldots, 2n + 1$. $L_2(R_n)$ denotes the usual Hilbert or L_2 space constructed from the Lebesgue $(2n + 1)$-dimensional measure restricted to R_n. In the proof of the next theorem we shall refer to necessary and sufficient conditions for the solvability of an infinite system of linear equations in the countable dimensional Hilbert space. For the convenience of the reader we have included a discussion of these conditions in Appendix B.

Theorem 1.14

If $f \in H_2(R_e z > 0)$ and n is a nonnegative integer, then there exists $k \in L_2(R_n)$ such that

$$f^{(n)}(z) = \int_0^\infty \int_0^\infty \cdots \int_0^\infty e^{-z(t_1 + \cdots + t_{2n+1})} k(t_1, \ldots, t_{2n+1}) \, dt_1 \, dt_2 \ldots dt_{2n+1},$$

where $f^{(n)}(z)$ denotes the nth derivative of f at z.

Proof. From Theorem 1.8 we have

$$f(z) = \int_0^\infty e^{-zt} h(t) \, dt;$$

hence, for $n > 0$,

$$f^{(n)}(z) = (-1)^n \int_0^\infty e^{-zt} t^n h(t) \, dt. \tag{1.14a}$$

If we now consider infinitely many distinct values for z, say z_j, set $\bar{g} = (-1)^n h$, and use the inner-product notation for the Hilbert space. (1.14a) tells us that the infinite system of linear equations

$$(e^{-z_j t} t^n, g) = f^{(n)}(z_j), \qquad j = 1, 2, \ldots, \tag{1.14b}$$

in the Hilbert space $L_2(0, \infty)$ has a nontrivial solution g. Now consider the infinite system of linear equations

$$(e^{-z_j(t_1 + \cdots + t_{2n+1})}, k) = f^{(n)}(z_j), \qquad j = 1, 2, \ldots, \tag{1.14c}$$

in the Hilbert space $L_2(R_n)$. Equation (B.1d) of Appendix B tells us that, aside from a multiplicative factor, the necessary condition for (1.14b) to be solvable is also the sufficient condition for (1.14c) to be solvable. Suppose

$k \in L_2(R_n)$ is the solution to (1.14c) and set

$$\varphi(z) = \int_0^\infty \int_0^\infty \cdots \int_0^\infty e^{-z(t_1 + \cdots + t_{2n+1})} k(t_1, \ldots, t_{2n+1}) \, dt_1 \ldots dt_{2n+1} \quad (1.14d)$$

so that $\varphi(z_j) = f^{(n)}(z_j)$, $j = 1, 2, \ldots$. We shall see that if the points z_j are suitably selected, then we can conclude that $\varphi \equiv f^{(n)}$. Suppose, therefore, we pick z_j so that $z_j = j + 2$. Using (1.14a) and (1.14d) we have, for $R_e z > 2$,

$$|\varphi(z) - f^{(n)}(z)| \le \left\{ \int_0^\infty \int_0^\infty \cdots \int_0^\infty |k(t_1 + \cdots t_{2n+1})|^2 \, dt_1 + \cdots + dt_{2n+1} \right\}^{1/2}$$

$$+ \left\{ \int_0^\infty |h(t)|^2 \, dt \right\}^{1/2} < \infty.$$

Hence, $\varphi - f^{(n)}$ is a bounded analytic function in the half-plane $R_e z > 2$. This together with Theorem 1.6.2 and the fact that $\varphi(j + 2) = f^{(n)}(j + 2)$, $j = 1, 2, \ldots$ implies $\varphi(z) = f^{(n)}(z)$ for $R_e z > 2$, which in turn, implies $\varphi(z) = f^{(n)}(z)$ for $R_e z > 0$.

We are now in a position to explain some of the differences between Theorems 1.12 and 1.13. First of all, the representation (1.14a) of $f^{(n)}$ as a multiple-dimensional Laplace transform of a function in $L_2(R_n)$ is by no means unique. For example, if $n = 1$, $0 < \alpha_j \ne 1$, $j = 1, 2, 3$; β_j, $j = 1, 2, 3$, a permutation of α_j, $k_1(t_1, t_2, t_3) = (1 + \alpha_1 t_1 + \alpha_2 t_2 + \alpha_3 t_3)^{-1}$, and $k_2(t_1, t_2, t_3) = (1 + \beta_1 t_1 + \beta_2 t_2 + \beta_3 t_3)^{-1}$, then upon substituting k_1 and k_2 in (1.14d), we see that they give rise to the same analytic function φ. Now the closure properties of $\{e^{-z_j t^n}\}_{j=1}^\infty$ are reflected in the distribution of the zeros of $f^{(n)}(z)$, which in turn and by Jensen's formula (Theorems 1.4 and 1.5), is controlled by the rate of growth of the modulus of $f^{(n)}$. In the case where $R_e z \to 0$, the behavior of $|f^{(n)}(z)|$ is entirely influenced by k, and the nonuniqueness of k is reflected in Theorem 1.12. In the case where $R_e z > \delta > 0$, $|f^{(n)}(z)|$ is controlled by $e^{-z(t_1 + \cdots + t_{2n+1})}$, and this accounts for Theorem 1.13. In case $n = 0$, Theorem 1.18 tells us that there is no problem of nonuniqueness, and this accounts for the differences between Theorems 1.11 and 1.12.

The families we have studied are also families of continuous functions and are associated with closure problems in certain Banach spaces of continuous function. We already noted (cf. Remark 1.1) that if $C[a,b]$ is the space of continuous functions on the finite interval $[a,b]$, then the dual space of $C[a,b]$ is the normalized function of bounded variation on $[a,b]$. If $a = -\infty$ or $b = \infty$ and $C_0[a,b]$ denotes the continuous functions f on

$[a,b]$ such that $|f(x)| \to 0$ as $|x| \to \infty$, $x \in [a,b]$, then a basic result due to Kakutani [40] asserts that the dual space of $C_0[a,b]$ is the normalized function of bounded variation φ on $[a,b]$ such that $\int_a^b |d\varphi| < \infty$. In fact, if $T \in C_0^*[a,b]$ we have

$$T(f) = \int_a^b f \, d\varphi$$

for $f \in C_0[a,b]$.

Theorem 1.15

If $\{z_j\}_{j=1}^\infty$ is a sequence of distinct numbers such that $R_e z_j > 0$, then a necessary and sufficient condition in order that $\{e^{-z_j t}\}_{j=1}^\infty$ be fundamental $C_0[0,\infty]$ is that the infinite series (1.11a) diverge.

Proof. If $\{e^{-z_j t}\}_{j=1}^\infty$ is fundamental in $C_0[0,\infty]$, then, since $C_0[0,\infty]$ is dense in $L_2(0,\infty)$, $\{e^{-z_j t}\}_{j=1}^\infty$ is fundamental in $L_2(0,\infty)$, and by Theorem 1.11 the series (1.11a) diverges. Suppose now that (1.11a) diverges and that $\{e^{-z_j t}\}_{j=1}^\infty$ is not fundamental in $C_0[0,\infty]$. Consequently, there exists a function φ of bounded variation on $[0,\infty]$ such that $\int_0^\infty |d\varphi| < \infty$ and

$$\int_0^\infty e^{-z_j t} \, d\varphi(t) = 0 \quad j = 1,2,\ldots.$$

If we set

$$f(z) = \int_0^\infty e^{-zt} \, d\varphi(t),$$

then $f \in H_\infty(R_e z > 0)$ and $f(z_j) = 0$. Hence the divergence of (1.11a) together with Theorem 1.6.2 implies that $f \equiv 0$ so that $f(n) = 0$, $n = 0,1,\ldots$. Under the transformation $t = -\ln u$, $0 \le u \le 1$, $\Psi(u) = \varphi(-\ln u)$, this becomes

$$\int_0^1 u^n \, d\Psi(u) = 0, \quad n = 0,1,\ldots.$$

Inasmuch as we can assume $\Psi(0) = 0$ we have, upon using the integration-by-parts formula,

$$\int_0^1 t^n \Psi(t) \, dt = 0, \quad n = 0,1,\ldots. \tag{1.15a}$$

At this stage of our argument we shall prove directly, rather than invoke the Weierstrass polynomial theorem, that (1.15a) implies $\Psi \equiv 0$ and thus obtain the Weierstrass theorem as a corollary. To this end, we can assume

Ψ is real-valued, $0 < t_0 < 1$, $\Psi(t_0) > 0$, and Ψ is continuous at t_0. Hence let $\delta > 0$ and $0 < \alpha < \beta < 1$ such that $\Psi(t) \geq \delta$ for $\alpha \leq t \leq \beta$, so that Ψ is continuous at α and β. Set $P(t) = 1 + d(\beta - t)(t - \alpha)$, where $d^{-1} = \sup\{|\alpha| \cdot |\beta - 1|, \;\; |\beta| \cdot |\alpha - 1|\}$. Therefore, $P(t) \geq 0$ for $0 \leq t \leq 1$, $P(\alpha) = P(\beta) = 1$, $P(t) > 1$ for $\alpha < t < \beta$, and $P(t) < 1$ for $0 \leq t < \alpha$ or $\beta < t \leq 1$. Hence

$$\liminf_n \int_0^1 \Psi(t)[P(t)]^n \, dt \geq \delta(\beta - \alpha) > 0,$$

which contradicts

$$\int_0^1 \Psi[P(t)]^n \, dt = 0$$

for all n and completes the proof of Theorem 1.14 [7].

The proof that (1.15a) implies $\Psi \equiv 0$ can be found in [20]. Also note in the argument that (1.15a) implies $\Psi \equiv 0$; we can replace [0,1] by [a,b] and change the definition of d so that $d^{-1} = \sup\{|\alpha - b| \cdot |\beta - b|, \; |\alpha - a| \cdot |\beta - a|\}$. Hence, we get the Weierstrass polynomial theorem as

Corollary 1.15.1
$\{t^n\}_{n=0}^\infty$ is fundamental in $C[a,b]$ where $-\infty < a < b < \infty$.

One of the first generalizations of Corollary 1.15.1 was due to Muntz and Szasz (cf. [57], [86], and [62]). It is

Theorem 1.16
If $\{z_j\}_{j=0}^\infty$ is a sequence of distinct numbers such that $z_0 = 0$ and $R_e z_j > 0$ for $j > 0$, then a necessary and sufficient condition in order that $\{t^{z_j}\}_{j=0}^\infty$ be fundamental in $C[0,1]$ is that the series (1.11a) diverge.

Proof. If $\{t^{z_j}\}_{j=0}^\infty$ is fundamental in $C[0,1]$, then $\{e^{-z_j u}\}_{j=1}^\infty$, $u = -\ln t$, is fundamental in $C_0[0,\infty]$ and by the previous theorem, (1.11a) is divergent. Suppose (1.11a) diverges and

$$\int_0^1 t^{z_j} \, d\Psi(t) = 0, \qquad j = 0,1,\ldots.$$

If

$$f(z) = \int_0^1 t^z \, d\Psi(t),$$

then $f \in H_\infty(R_e z > 0)$ and by Theorem 1.6.2 $f \equiv 0$. This leads to (1.15a).

There are analogues of Theorems 1.12 and 1.13 for the families of functions and function spaces appearing in Theorems 1.15 and 1.16. Finally, it is worth noting that the underlying space on which the functions of the function families are defined plays an important role. To illustrate this point, we note that $\{t^{2n}\}_{n=0}^\infty$ is not fundamental in $C[-1,1]$; in fact, no function of the form t^{2m+1}, $m = 0,1,\ldots$ can be uniformly approximated on $[-1,1]$ by linear combinations out of $\{t^{2n}\}_{n=0}^\infty$ (and vice versa) on $[-1,1]$. The verification of all the above assertions is left to the reader.

Chapter 2

FUNCTIONS WITH
POSITIVE REAL PART

IN THIS CHAPTER we shall present representation theorems for analytic functions with positive real part and exploit the properties of these functions in order to (a) get further structure theorems for the class of functions with bounded log mean, and (b) study some particular problems in the theory of approximation and interpolation.

Theorem 2.1

If f is analytic on $|x| < 1$, then f has positive real part if and only if there exists a nondecreasing function φ on $[0,2\pi]$ such that

$$f(x) = i\lambda + \int_0^{2\pi} \frac{e^{it} + x}{e^{it} - x} \, d\varphi(t), \tag{2.1a}$$

where $\lambda = I_m f(0)$; moreover, if $\varphi(0) = 0$ and φ is normalized, then φ is uniquely determined by f.

Proof. If f has the representation of (2.1a) and $x = re^{i\theta}$, then

$$R_e f(x) = \int_0^{2\pi} \frac{1 - r^2}{1 - 2r \cos(\theta - t) + r^2} \, d\varphi(t) \geq 0.$$

Conversely, let $R_e f(x) \geq 0$ and

$$f(x) = \sum_{p=0}^{\infty} (a_p + ib_p)x^p.$$

30

We set

$$\varphi_r(t) = \frac{1}{2\pi} \int_0^t R_e f(re^{i\theta})\, d\theta$$

so that φ_r is nondecreasing for every r, $\varphi_r(0) = 0$, $\varphi_r(2\pi) = R_e f(0)$!

and

$$\int_0^{2\pi} 2 \cos pt\, d\varphi_r(t) = r^p a_p, \qquad p = 1,2,\ldots,$$

$$\int_0^{2\pi} -2 \sin pt\, d\varphi_r(t) = r^p b_p, \qquad p = 1,2,\ldots.$$

It now follows (cf. Remark 1.0) that there exist a sequence $\{r_n\}_{n=1}^{\infty}$ such that $0 < r_n < r_{n+1} \to 1$ as $n \to \infty$, and a nondecreasing function φ on $[0,2\pi]$ such that $\varphi_{r_n}(t) \to \varphi(t)$ as $n \to \infty$,

$$\int_0^{2\pi} 2 \cos pt\, d\varphi(t) = a_p, \qquad p = 1,2,\ldots,$$

and

$$\int_0^{2\pi} -2 \sin pt\, d\varphi(t) = b_p, \qquad p = 1,2,\ldots.$$

If we substitute these expressions for the values of a_p and b_p in the series expansion for f, we get

$$f(x) = ib_0 + \int_0^{2\pi} \left\{ 1 + 2 \sum_p (x^p e^{-ipt}) \right\} d\varphi(t)$$

$$= ib_0 + \int_0^{2\pi} \frac{e^{it} + x}{e^{it} - x}\, d\varphi(t).$$

To prove the uniqueness of the function φ, let us suppose that Ψ is a real-valued and normalized function of bounded variation such that

$$\int_0^{2\pi} \cos p\theta\, d\Psi(\theta) = \int_0^{2\pi} \sin p\theta\, d\Psi(\theta) = \Psi(2\pi) = 0, \qquad p = 0,1,\ldots.$$

This implies that

$$\int_0^{2\pi} e^{in\theta} \, d\Psi(\theta) = 0, \qquad n = 0, \pm 1, \pm 2, \ldots .$$

If

$$f(w) = \int_0^{2\pi} e^{w\theta} \, d\Psi(\theta),$$

then f is bounded analytic $R_e w < 1$ and $f(in) = 0$. Under the transformation $w = 2z(1 - z)^{-1}$, f maps into a bounded analytic function on $|z| < 1$ and, in view of Corollary 1.3, $f \equiv 0$. This implies that

$$\int_0^\infty e^{-x\theta} \, d\sigma(\theta) = 0$$

for $x \geq 0$ and where $\sigma(\theta) = \Psi(\theta)$, $0 \leq \theta \leq 2\pi$, and $\sigma(\theta) = \Psi(2\pi)$, $2\pi \leq \theta$. This again leads to a system of equations similar to (1.15a) and completes the proof of Theorem 2.1.

The proof of Theorem 2.1 gives us the Weierstrass approximation theorem involving trigonometric polynomials.

Corollary 2.1.1
    The family $\{e^{-int}\}_{n=-\infty}^{\infty}$ is fundamental in $C[0,2\pi]$.

Remark 2.0. The kernel $k(x,t) = (e^{it} + x)(e^{it} - x)^{-1}$ is usually called the *complex Poisson kernel*. Theorem 2.1 is a fundamental result of Herglotz and F. Riesz [74]. The proof we presented comes from [92], pp. 275–276. For extensions of Theorem 2.1 to locally compact abelian groups see [5] and [71]. For the extension of Corollary 2.1.1 to compact abelian groups see [58], p. 425.

From Theorem 2.1 we get

Theorem 2.2
    If f is analytic on $|x| < 1$ and real for real x, then f has positive real part if and only if

$$f(x) = \frac{1 + x}{1 - x} \int_0^{2\pi} \left\{ 1 + \frac{4x}{(1 - x)^2} \sin^2 \frac{t}{2} \right\}^{-1} d\varphi(t), \qquad (2.2a)$$

where φ is nondecreasing on $[0,2\pi]$; moreover, if $\varphi(0) = 0$ and φ is normalized, then φ is uniquely determined by f.[1]

The following corollary follows from the proof of Theorem 2.1.

Corollary 2.2.1
If f is analytic on $|x| < 1$, then f can be represented in the form of (2.1a) with φ replaced by a real-valued function of bounded variation if and only if

$$\sup_{r} \int_{0}^{2\pi} |R_e f(re^{i\theta})| \, d\theta < \infty; \tag{2.2b}$$

if f satisfies (2.2b) and is real for real x, then (and only then) f can be represented in the form (2.2a) with φ replaced by a real-valued function of bounded variation.

To obtain the next representation theorem let us recall that the transformation $z = 4x(1 - x)^{-2}$ with inverse $x = (\sqrt{1 + z} - 1)(\sqrt{1 + z} + 1)^{-1}$ and $\sqrt{1} = 1$ maps $|x| < 1$ conformally onto $\text{ext}[-\infty, -1]$.

Theorem 2.3
If f is analytic on $\text{ext}[-\infty, -1]$ and real for real z, then f has positive real part if and only if

$$f(z) = \sqrt{1 + z} \int_{0}^{1} (1 + zu)^{-1} \, d\varphi(u), \tag{2.3a}$$

where φ is nondecreasing on $[0,1]$; moreover, under the usual normalization φ is uniquely determined by f ([92], p. 279).

---

[1] Under the hypothesis of Theorem 2.2, we have for real x,

$$f(x) = \int_{0}^{2\pi} \frac{1 - x^2 - 2i \sin t}{1 - 2x \cos t + x^2} \, d\varphi(t)$$

$$= \int_{0}^{2\pi} \frac{1 - x^2}{1 - 2x \cos t + x^2} \, d\varphi(t).$$

Also,

$$\frac{1 - x^2}{1 - 2x \cos t + x^2} = \frac{1 - x^2}{(1 - x)^2 + 4x \sin^2(t/2)}.$$

Proof. Suppose g is analytic on $|x| < 1$ and $f(z) = f(4x(1 - x)^{-2}) = g(x)$. Then f satisfies the hypothesis of Theorem 2.3 if and only if g satisfies the hypothesis of Theorem 2.2. In accordance with Theorem 2.2,

$$f(z) = \frac{1 + x}{1 - x} \int_0^{2\pi} \left\{ 1 + \frac{4x}{(1 - x)^2} \sin^2 \frac{t}{2} \right\} d\varphi(t)$$

$$= \sqrt{1 + z} \int_0^{2\pi} \left\{ 1 + z \sin^2 \frac{t}{2} \right\}^{-1} d\varphi(t).$$

For $|z| < 1$, the preceding formula gives us

$$f(z) = \sqrt{1 + z} \left(\sum_{p=0}^{\infty} a_p (-1)^p z^p \right)$$

where

$$a_p = \int_0^{2\pi} \left(\sin^2 \frac{t}{2} \right)^p d\varphi(t), \qquad p = 0,1,\ldots.$$

In accordance with (C.1d) of Appendix C the sequence $\{a_p\}_{p=0}^{\infty}$ is a moment sequence and

$$a_p = \int_0^1 u^p \, d\sigma(u),$$

where σ is nondecreasing on $[0,1]$. Substituting these expressions for the values of a_p in the power-series expansion of f gives

$$f(z) = \sqrt{1 + z} \int_0^1 \frac{1}{1 + zu} \, d\sigma(u)$$

for $|z| < 1$. Since the right side of the last expression defines a function which is analytic on $\text{ext}[-\infty, -1]$, we have (2.3a). The uniqueness of φ in (2.3a) follows from Corollary 1.15.1, with $a = 0$ and $b = 1$.

The following corollary will be needed later.

Corollary 2.3.1

If f is bounded and analytic on $\text{ext}[-\infty, -1]$ and real for real z, then there exists uniquely a normalized function φ of bounded variation on $[0,1]$ such that $\varphi(0) = 0$ and

$$f(z) = \sqrt{1 + z} \int_0^1 (1 + zu)^{-1} \, d\varphi(u). \tag{2.3b}$$

Proof. Set $f = M - (M - f)$, where $M > \sup_z |f(z)|$, so that f is the difference of two functions represented by (2.3a).

It is possible to solve (2.3b) for φ and φ' in terms of f. With a view toward later applications we shall do this now.

Theorem 2.4

If f is analytic on $\text{ext}[-\infty, -1]$, φ a real-valued and normalized function of bounded variation on $[0,1]$, and

$$f(z) = \int_0^1 (1 + zu)^{-1} \, d\varphi(u)$$

for $z \in \text{ext}[-\infty, -1]$, then

$$\lim_{y \to 0^+} \frac{-1}{\pi} \int_v^u \frac{1}{t} I_m f \left(-\frac{1}{t} + iy \right) dt = \frac{\varphi(u) - \varphi(v)}{2} \tag{2.4a}$$

for $0 \le v < u \le 1$, and

$$\lim_{y \to 0^+} \frac{-1}{\pi t} I_m \left(-\frac{1}{t} + iy \right) = \varphi'(t) \tag{2.4b}$$

for any $t \in (0,1)$ such that $\varphi'(t)$ exists.

Proof. We shall establish (2.4b) first, and its proof is similar to the proof of Lemma 1.6.3. If $\varphi'(t_0)$ exists, $R(t) = [(t_0 - t)^2 + (t_0 y t)^2]^{-1}$, and $s = t_0 \pi^{-1}$, then

$$\frac{-1}{\pi t_0} I_m f \left(-\frac{1}{t_0} + iy \right) = sy \int_0^{t_0} t R(t) \, d\varphi(t) + sy \int_{t_0}^1 t R(t) \, d\varphi(t). \tag{2.4c}$$

If we replace $\varphi(t)$ by $[\varphi(t_0) + \varphi'(t_0)(t - t_0) + h(t)(t - t_0)]$, then h is a bounded function, h is continuous at t_0, $h(t_0) = 0$, and the first integral in (2.4c) becomes

$$\varphi'(t_0) sy \int_0^{t_0} t R(t) \, dt + sy \int_0^{t_0} t R(t) \, dh(t)(t - t_0).$$

The first term in the last expression can be integrated directly and we can easily verify that it approaches $2^{-1}\phi'(t_0)$ as $y \to 0^+$. Upon using the integration-by-parts formula, the second term reduces to

$$-sy \int_0^{t_0} h(t)(t - t_0)[R(t) + tR'(t)]\, dt.$$

The absolute value of this last expression is less than

$$\frac{2y}{\pi} \int_0^{t_0} |h(t)| R(t)\, dt.$$

For $\varepsilon > 0$, there exists $\delta > 0$ such that $|h(t)| < \frac{1}{2}\varepsilon t_0^2$ for $0 \le t_0 - t < \delta$, so that

$$\frac{2y}{\pi} \int_{t_0-\delta}^{t_0} |h(t)| R(t)\, dt < \frac{2\varepsilon y t_0^2}{\pi} \int_0^1 R(t)\, dt < \varepsilon$$

for $y > 0$. Since h is a bounded function, there exists $y_0 > 0$ such that $0 < y < y_0$ implies

$$\frac{2y}{\pi} \int_0^{t_0-\delta} |h(t)| R(t)\, dt < \varepsilon.$$

The second integral in (2.4c) is treated in a similar manner and, therefore, (2.4b) is established. Equation (2.4a) is established by evaluating

$$\frac{t_0 y}{\pi} \int_0^1 \int_v^u \frac{1}{t[(t - t_0)^2 + (t_0 y t)^2]}\, dy\, d\varphi(t).$$

The details are left to the reader.

Theorem 2.4 is a variation on a classical inversion formula due to Stieltjes (cf. [92], p. 250). A milder form of (2.4a) is in [97] p. 340. Equations (2.4a) and (2.4b) come from [66].

In the proof of Theorem 1.6.2 and in subsequent arguments we use the fact that a function which is a linear combination of functions with positive real part is necessarily the ratio of two bounded functions and, therefore, had bounded log mean when mapped into a function on $|x| < 1$. At this time we shall give a characterization of the class of functions that are the ratio of two bounded functions. This class has several names; e.g., *Nevanlinna class, functions with bounded characteristic, beschränktartige functions,* and *functions with bounded log$^+$ mean.* Nevanlinna's penetrating study of this and a larger class of functions ranks as one of the outstanding achievements of function theory. We cannot go into the depth of this theory and our immediate goal is to quickly characterize the analytic functions with bounded log$^+$ mean and to show, in a measure theoretic sense which will be made more precise later, that the boundedness of the log$^+$ mean of f is equivalent to boundedness of the log mean of certain translates of f.

Recall that if $a > 0$, then $\log^+ a = 0$ or $\log a$, according as to $a \leq 1$ or $a > 1$.

Definition 2.1. If f is analytic on $|x| < 1$, then f is said to be "beschränktartige" (or have bounded characteristic) if and only if

$$\sup_{r<1} \int_0^{2\pi} \log^+ |f(re^{i\theta})| \, d\theta < \infty.$$

We denote this sup $L^+(f,1)$. $L^+(f,r)$ denotes $L^+(f_r,1)$, where $f_r(x) = f(rx)$, $r < 1$, and $|x| < 1$.

Theorem 2.5

If f is analytic on $|x| < 1$, then f is beschränktartige if and only if

$$f = Be^{(h-k)}$$

where B is the Blaschke product formed from the zeros of f and h and k are analytic and have positive real part on $|x| < 1$.

Proof. If $f = Be^{h-k}$, then

$$\int_0^{2\pi} \log^+ |f(re^{i\theta})| \, d\theta \leq \int_0^{2\pi} R_e\{h(re^{i\theta}) + k(re^{i\theta})\} \, d\theta$$

$$\leq 2\pi\{h(0) + k(0)\}$$

and $L^+(f,1) < \infty$. If $L^+(f,1) < \infty$, then, by Corollary 1.5.1, $f = Be^g$ and, in accordance with Corollary 2.2.1, we only need to show that

$$\sup_r \int_0^{2\pi} |R_e g(re^{i\theta})| \, d\theta < \infty.$$

This amounts to an easy computation, which is left to the reader.

Theorem 2.6

If f is analytic on $|x| < 1$, then f is beschränktartige if and only if $f = p/q$, where each of p and q is bounded and analytic on $|x| < 1$.

Proof. If $L^+(f,1) < \infty$ and $f = Be^{h-k}$, then set $p = Be^{-k}$ and $q = e^{-h}$. If $f = p/q$, then

$$L^+(f,1) \le \left(\sup_{|x| < 1} |p(x)| + \sup_{|x| < 1} |q(x)| \right) 2\pi \le 2\pi(\|p\|_\infty + \|q\|_\infty).$$

We now turn our attention to the statement made earlier that the log mean and $\log^+$ mean are equivalent in a suitable measure theoretic sense. To this end we shall ascertain under what additional conditions $L(f,1) < \infty$ implies $L^+(f,1) < \infty$. The problem is quite deep and requires measure theoretic concepts that combine the topological structure and the field structure of the complex plane. The concept we employ is that of "capacity," and we shall develop only the capacity theorems we need. Before doing this, however, we shall illustrate our goal with the statements of two preliminary theorems (Theorems 2.7 and 2.8). These theorems are special cases and we shall discuss them instead of giving proofs.

Theorem 2.7

Suppose f is analytic on $|x| < 1$, λ a complex number, and $f_\lambda(x) = f(x) - \lambda$. Then $L^+(f,1) < \infty$ if and only if $L(f_\lambda,1) < \infty$ for every λ.

The proof of Theorem 2.7 uses the fact that the planar Lebesgue measure is translation-invariant on the set of numbers λ under consideration. It is important to know that we can restrict λ to a set smaller than the plane.

Theorem 2.8

Suppose f is analytic on $|x| < 1$ and K a continuum in the plane. Then $L^+(f,1) < \infty$ if and only if $L(f_\lambda,1) < \infty$ for every λ in K.

The proof of Theorem 2.8 uses the fact that K is connected and projects on some straight line L in a set of nonzero linear measure and finally that the measure is translation-invariant on L. A continuum, however, is too large a set and it is possible to get by in Theorem 2.8 with a smaller set, e.g., the classical Cantor set on $[0,1]$.

To develop the theory of capacity let us recall that if E is a compact subset of the complex plane, then the Borel algebra generated by E is the smallest sigma algebra, say Σ, containing all compact subsets of E. A

Borel measure on E is a countably additive function from Σ to the complex numbers. A Borel measure μ on E is called *regular* if for any Borel set $K \subset E$ and $\varepsilon > 0$ there exists set F and 0 in E such that F is compact, 0 is open (relative to E), $F \subset K \subset 0$, $|\mu(K - F)| < \varepsilon$, and $|\mu(0 - F)| < \varepsilon$. The collection of all regular Borel measures on E is denoted by $M(E)$ and $M(E)$ is the dual space of $C(E)$, the continuous functions on E (cf. [20]). A probability measure μ on E is a regular Borel measure on E such that

$$0 \leq \mu(K) \leq \mu(E) = 1$$

for $K \in \Sigma$. Our development of the theory of capacity follows that of Tsuji [90] and Hille [34].

Definition 2.2. Suppose E is a compact set of the complex plane and μ a probability measure on E. The function $U(z,\mu)$ defined by

$$U(z,\mu) = \int_E \log|z - t|^{-1} \, d\mu(t)$$

is called the *logarithmic potential* of E and μ. The number (possibly ∞)

$$I(\mu) = \int_E \int_E \log|s - t|^{-1} \, d\mu(t) \, d\mu(s)$$

is called the *energy integral* of μ.

The integrals in the above definition are interpreted in the sense that

$$\lim_n \int_E \{\log|z - t|^{-1}\}_n \, d\mu(t)$$

and

$$\lim_n \int_E \int_E \{\log|z - t|^{-1}\}_n \, d\mu(t) \, d\mu(s)$$

where $\{\log|s - t|^{-1}\}_n = \log|z - t|^{-1}$, n or $-n$, according to $|\log|z - t|^{-1}| \leq n$, $\log|z - t|^{-1} > n$, or $\log|z - t|^{-1} < -n$. The function $U(z,\mu)$ satisfies $-\infty \leq U(z,\mu) < \infty$ for every z, is harmonic on the complement of E, and is lower-semicontinuous on the entire complex plane [note that

$$U(z,\mu) = \lim_n U_n(z,\mu)$$

and $U_n(z,\mu) = \int_E \{\log|z - t|^{-1}\}_n \, d\mu(t)$ is a continuous function of z].

The following theorem (*maximum principle for logarithmic potentials*) is due to Maria [49]. Unless stated otherwise, the set E will be a fixed compact subset of the complex plane.

Theorem 2.9

If M is a real number such that $U(z,\mu) \leq M$ for $z \in E$, then $U(z,\mu) \leq M$ for every complex number z.

Proof. Let K be the complement E. $U(z,\mu)$ is harmonic on K and $\lim_{|z| \to \infty} U(z,\mu) = -\infty$, so by the classical maximum modulus theorem applied to harmonic functions, we need only show that $U(z,\mu) \leq M$ for z in any neighborhood of $E \cap \bar{K}$, where $\bar{K}$ is the closure of K, and, moreover, we shall show this for one of the components K_0 of K; i.e., if $a \in E \cap \bar{K}_0$, then $\limsup_{z \to a, z \in K_0} U(z,\mu) \leq M$. First note that μ is purely continuous, for if $z_0 \in E$ and $\mu(\{z_0\}) > 0$, then $U(z_0,\mu) = \infty$, which contradicts the hypothesis. Hence, for $\varepsilon > 0$ there exists a neighborhood N_ε of a such that $\mu(N_\varepsilon) < \varepsilon$. For $\rho > 0$ let N_ρ denote the set $[z; |z - a| < \rho]$, $K_\rho = N_\rho \cap K_0$, and $E_\rho = N_\rho \cap E$. Pick ρ small enough so that $E_\rho \subset N_\varepsilon$. Suppose now $z \in K_\rho$. There exists $\xi \in K_\rho$ such that $|z - \xi| \leq |z - t|$ for $t \in E_\rho$ and, consequently, $|\xi - t| \leq |z - t| + |\xi - z| \leq 2|z - t|$ for $t \in E_\rho$. Hence

$$\int_{E_\rho} \log|z - t|^{-1} \, d\mu(t) \leq (\log 2)\mu(E_\rho) + \int_{E_\rho} \log|\xi - t|^{-1} \, d\mu(t)$$

$$\leq (\log 2)\mu(E_\rho) + \int_E \log|\xi - t|^{-1} \, d\mu(t) - \int_{E - E_\rho} \log|\xi - t|^{-1} \, d\mu(t),$$

or

$$\int_E \log|z - t|^{-1} \, d\mu(t) \leq \varepsilon \log 2 + M + \int_{E - E_\rho} \log\left|\frac{\xi - t}{z - t}\right| d\mu(t).$$

As $z \to a$, $\xi \to a$, and $\log|(\xi - t)/(z - t)| \to 0$. Hence

$$\limsup_{\substack{z \to a \\ z \in K_0}} U(z, \mu) \leq M.$$

Definition 2.3. If E is a compact subset of the complex plane, then the capacity $r(E)$ of E is defined as

$$-\log r(E) = \inf_\mu I(\mu),$$

where $I(\mu)$ is defined as in Definition 2.2 and the inf is taken over all probability measures μ such that μ is supported in E; i.e., $\mu \in M(E)$. If V denotes

$\inf_\mu I(\mu)$, then $r(E) = e^{-V}$ and $r(E) \geq 0$. $r(E) = 0$ if and only if $V = \infty$. If E' is just a Borel set, then $r(E') = \sup_{E \subset E'} r(E)$, E compact.

Theorem 2.10

If $V < \infty$, then there exists a probability measure $\mu \in M(E)$ such that $V = I(\mu)$.

Proof. Suppose $V = \lim_n I(\mu_n)$, $\mu_n \in M(E)$, $\mu_n \geq 0$, and $\mu_n(E) = 1$. By the weak star compactness of $M(E)$, there exists a $\mu \in M(E)$ and an increasing sequence n_p such that

$$\int_E f(t)\, d\mu_{n_p}(t) \to \int_E f(t)\, d\mu(t)$$

for every continuous function $f(t)$ on E. The function $\{\log|z - t|^{-1}\}_m$ is a continuous function of both z and t; hence

$$\int_E \int_E \{\log|z - t|^{-1}\}_m\, d\mu(t)\, d\mu(z)$$

$$= \lim_p \int_E \int_E \{\log|z - t|^{-1}\}_m\, d\mu_{n_p}(t)\, d\mu_{n_p}(z)$$

$$\leq \lim_p \int_E \int_E \log|z - t|^{-1}\, d\mu_{n_p}(t)\, d\mu_{n_p}(z) = \lim_p I(\mu_{n_p}) = V.$$

It follows, therefore, upon letting $m \to \infty$, that $I(\mu) \leq V$. On the other hand, by the definition of V, $V \leq I(\mu)$. Consequently, $V = I(\mu)$.

The measure μ in the conclusion of Theorem 2.10 is, in fact, unique. Inasmuch as we do not need the uniqueness, we shall leave its proof to the reader.

The measure μ of Theorem 2.10 is usually called the *equilibrium distribution* of E and, for this μ, $U(z,\mu)$ is called the *equilibrium potential*.

We list several interesting properties of $r(E)$. The proofs are left to the reader.

Theorem 2.11

If $E_1 \subset E_2$, then $r(E_1) \leq r(E_2)$.

Theorem 2.12

If $w = \alpha z + \beta$ and $E_1 = [w; w = \alpha z + \beta, z \in E]$, then $r(E_1) = |\alpha| r(E)$; i.e., capacity is invariant under rigid motions of the plane.

Theorem 2.13

If E is a continuum, then $r(E) > 0$.

Proof. Our interest in Theorem 2.13 is just in the case where E is an interval, say $[a, b]$. In this case it is obvious that

$$\int_a^b \int_a^b \log|s - t|^{-1}\, dt\, ds < \infty.$$

The proof of the general case is left to the reader.

Theorem 2.14

Suppose $E_1 \subset E$, $r(E_1) = 0$, $r(E) > 0$, $\mu \in M(E)$, and

$$I(\mu) = \int_E \int_E \log|z - t|^{-1}\, d\mu(t)\, d\mu(z) < \infty;$$

then $\mu(E_1) = 0$.

Proof. Suppose $\sup_{z,t \in E} |z - t| \le 1$. Then $\log|z - t|^{-1} \ge 0$ and

$$\int_{E_1} \int_{E_1} \log|z - t|^{-1}\, d\mu(t)\, d\mu(z) \le \int_E \int_E \log|z - t|^{-1}\, d\mu(t)\, d\mu(z) < \infty.$$

Hence, if $\mu(E_1) = \alpha > 0$, then $\alpha^{-1}\mu$ is a probability measure on E_1 and $r(E_1) > 0$. This contradiction proves Theorem 2.14.

One consequence of Theorem 2.14 is that if $r(E) = 0$, then the planar measure of $E = 0$. Theorem 2.13 (take $E = [0,1]$) shows that the converse is not true. An immediate consequence of Theorem 2.14 is

Lemma 2.14.1

If $F \subset \cup E_n$ and $r(E_n) = 0$, then $r(F) = 0$.

We now come to the fundamental theorem concerning capacity. The theorem is due to Frostman (cf. [22]).

Theorem 2.15

Suppose E is a compact subset of the complex plane, μ its equilibrium distribution, $r(E) > 0$, and $r(E) = e^{-v}$. Then for $z \in E$, $U(z,\mu) = v$ except at most for z belonging to a set $F \subset E$ such that $r(F) = 0$ and $U(z,\mu) \le v$ for every z in the complex plane.

Proof. Suppose F denotes the set of $z \in E$ such that $U(z,\mu) < v$ and that $r(F) > 0$. Let F_n denote the set of $z \in E$ such that $U(z,\mu) \leq v - (1/n)$. Then $F \subset \bigcup_n F_n$, F_n is compact in virtue of the lower semicontinuity of $U(z,\mu)$, and, by Lemma 2.13.1, $r(F_n) > 0$ for at least one n. Hence, there exists $\varepsilon > 0$ and a compact subset E_1 of E such that $U(z,\mu) < v - 2\varepsilon$ for $z \in E_1$. If K denotes the carrier of μ in E, then, since

$$\int_K U(z, \mu) \, d\mu = v$$

and $U(z,\mu)$ is lower-semicontinuous, there exists at $z_0 \in K$ and a neighborhood N of z_0 such that $E_1 \cap N = 0$, $U(z,\mu) > v - \varepsilon$, and $\mu(N) = m > 0$. Since $r(E_1) > 0$, the equilibrium distribution, say σ, for E_1 satisfies

$$\int_{E_1} \int_{E_1} \log|z - t|^{-1} \, d\sigma(t) \, d\sigma(z) < \infty.$$

Let v be the measure supported on E satisfying $v(H) = m\sigma(H)$ for $H \subset E_1$ and $v(H) = -\mu(H)$ for $H \subset N$; hence $v(E_1) = m$, $v(N) = -m$, and $v(H) = 0$ for $H \cap (E_1 \cup N) = 0$. Now we set $\beta = \mu + hv$, where $0 < h < 1$, $\beta(E) = 1$, and $\beta \geq 0$. A simple computation gives

$$0 \leq \int_{E_1} \int_{E_1} \log|z - t|^{-1} \, d\beta(t) \, d\beta(z) - \int_{E_1} \int_{E_1} \log|z - t|^{-1} \, d\mu(t) \, d\mu(z)$$

$$= 2h \left(\int_{E_1} U(z,\mu) \, dv + \int_N U(z,\mu) \, dv \right) + h^2 \int_{E_1} \int_{E_1} \log|z - t|^{-1} \, dv(t) \, dv(z)$$

$$< 2h[m(v - 2\varepsilon) - m(v - \varepsilon)] + h^2 \int_{E_1} \int_{E_1} \log|z - t|^{-1} \, dv(t) \, dv(z),$$

which can be made negative for small values of h. This contradiction shows that $r(E_1) = 0$. Hence, $U(z,\mu) \geq v$ for $z \in E - F$ and $r(F) = 0$.

Suppose now $z_0 \in K$, K the carrier of μ, and $U(z_0,\mu) > v$. Since $U(z,\mu)$ is lower-semicontinuous, we have $U(z,\mu) > v + \varepsilon$ for some neighborhood N of z_0. In view of Theorem 2.14 and the first part of this theorem we get

$$v = \int_E \int_E \log|z - t|^{-1} \, d\mu(t) \, d\mu(z) = \int_{K \cap N} U(z,\mu) \, d\mu(z) + \int_{K - N} U(z,\mu) \, d\mu(z)$$

$$> (v + \varepsilon)\mu(K \cap N) + V[1 - \mu(K \cap N)] = v + \varepsilon\mu(K \cap N) > V$$

which is an absurdity. Hence, $U(z,\mu) \leq v$ for $z \in K$. It follows now, from Theorem 2.9, that $U(z,\mu) \leq V$ for every z.

We turn now to the promised generalization of Theorems 2.8 and 2.9. The development we shall present is due to Mooney ([54], p. 172).

Theorem 2.16

If E is a compact subset of the complex plane, then $r(E) > 0$ if and only if there exist a finite nonnegative measure β supported on E and a $M > 0$ such that

$$\int_E \log^- |z - t| \, d\beta(t) < M$$

for every complex number z, where $\log^- = \log^+ - \log$.

Proof. Suppose such a number M and measure β exist. Then since $-\log a \le \log^- a$ for $a > 0$, we get

$$\int_E \int_E \log|z - t|^{-1} \, d\beta(t) \, d\beta(E) \le \int_E \left\{ \int_E \log^- |z - t| \, d\beta(t) \right\} d\beta(z) \le M\beta(E) < \infty.$$

This implies that

$$V = \inf_{\substack{\sigma \ge 0 \\ \sigma(E) = 1}} I(\sigma, E) < \infty,$$

and $r(E) = e^{-V} > 0$.

Suppose now that $r(E) > 0$ and μ is the equilibrium distribution of E. By Theorem 2.15,

$$U(z, \mu) = \int_E \log|z - t|^{-1} \, d\mu(t) \le V$$

for every complex number z. Fix z_0. If $|z_0 - t| \ge 1$ for every $t \in E$, then $\log^- |z_0 - t| = 0$ and

$$\int_E \log^- |z_0 - t| \, d\mu = 0 < \infty.$$

On the other hand, if $d(z_0, E) = \inf_{t \in E} |z_0 - t| < 1$, we have, with $\delta(E) = \sup_{t, t' \in E} |t - t'| = $ diameter of E, that $\log^+ |z_0 - t| \le \log|1 + \delta(E)|$ for $t \in E$ and

$$\int_E \log^- |z_0 - t| \, d\mu(t) = -\int_E \log|z_0 - t| \, d\mu(t) + \int_E \log^+ |z_0 - t| \, d\mu(t)$$

$$\le V + \delta(E).$$

Theorem 2.17

Suppose f is analytic on $|x| < 1$. Then f is beschränktartige if and only if there exists a compact set E such that $r(E) > 0$ and $L(f_\lambda, 1) < \infty$ for $\lambda \in E$, where $f_\lambda(x) = f(x) - \lambda$.

Note. The quantity $L(f_\lambda, 1)$ is a measurement of how often the function f takes on the value λ and is intimately connected with the structure of the Riemann surface of f. In our presentation we are nowhere near the depth of the Nevanlinna theory (cf. [59] and [28]). Also in connection with Theorem 2.17 see Example 1.2 and its subsequent application to Theorem 1.12, etc.

Proof. Since $r(E) > 0$ we have, by Theorem 2.16, that there exists a $M > 0$ and a finite nonnegative measure β carried on E such that

$$\int_E \log^- |f(re^{i\theta}) - \lambda| \, d\beta(\lambda) < M.$$

Let E_n denote the set of $\lambda \in E$ such that $L(f_\lambda, 1) \le n$; then $E \subset \bigcup_n E_n$ and, by Lemma 2.14.1, there exists E_n such that $r(E_n) > 0$. Hence

$$\int_{E_n} \frac{1}{2\pi} \int_0^{2\pi} \log^+ |f(re^{i\theta}) - \lambda| \, d\theta \, d\beta(\lambda) = \int_{E_n} \frac{1}{2\pi} \int_0^{2\pi} \log |f(re^{i\theta}) - \lambda| \, d\theta \, d\beta(\lambda)$$

$$+ \int_{E_n} \frac{1}{2\pi} \int_0^{2\pi} \log^- |f(re^{i\theta}) - \lambda| \, d\theta \, d\beta(\lambda)$$

$$\le n\beta(E_n) + M.$$

For $\lambda, \lambda_0 \in E_n$, we have $\left| \log^+ |z - \lambda| - \log^+ |z - \lambda_0| \right| \le \log(1 + |\lambda - \lambda_0|) \le \log(1 + \delta(E_n)) \le \delta(E_n)$, where $\delta(E_n) =$ diameter of E_n. Therefore,

$$\left| \frac{1}{2\pi} \int_0^{2\pi} (\log^+ |f(re^{i\theta}) - \lambda| - \log^+ |f(re^{i\theta}) - \lambda_0|) \, d\theta \right| \le \delta(E_n)$$

and

$$\frac{1}{2\pi} \int_0^{2\pi} \log^+ |f(re^{i\theta}) - \lambda_0| \, d\theta = \frac{1}{\beta(E_n)} \int_{E_n} \frac{1}{2\pi} \int_0^{2\pi} \log^+ |f(re^{i\theta}) - \lambda_0| \, d\theta \, d\beta(\lambda)$$

$$\le \frac{1}{\beta(E_n)} \int_{E_n} \frac{1}{2\pi} \int_0^{2\pi} \log^+ |f(re^{i\theta}) - \lambda| \, d\theta \, d\mu(\lambda)$$

$$+ \frac{1}{\beta(E_n)} \int_{E_n} \delta(E_n) \, d\beta(\lambda)$$

$$\le \frac{1}{\beta(E_n)} (n\beta(E_n) + M) + \delta(E_n).$$

Hence $L^+(f_{\lambda_0},1) \leq n + M + \delta(E_n)$, and, by Theorem 2.6,

$$f(x) - \lambda_0 = \frac{k_1(x)}{k_2(x)} \qquad \text{or} \qquad f(x) = \frac{\lambda_0 k_2(x) + k_1(x)}{k_2(x)}$$

which, again by Theorem 2.6, means f is beschränktartige.

We shall now use the theory of functions of positive real part to study fundamental families of functions in various function spaces. Specifically, we consider the family $\{(1 + k_p t)^{-1}\}_{p=0}^\infty$, $0 \neq k_p$, $k_p \neq k_q$ for $p \neq q$, and $k_p \in \text{ext}[-\infty, -1]$. We shall give conditions for $\{(1 + k_p t)^{-1}\}_{p=0}^\infty$ to be fundamental in $C[0,1]$ and $L_p[0,1]$, $1 \leq p < \infty$. In what follows, K denotes the linear manifold generated by $\{(1 + k_p t)^{-1}\}_{p=0}^\infty$ in $C[0,1]$ and K_p denotes the linear manifold generated by the same family in $L_p(0,1)$. $\bar{K}$ and $\bar{K}_p$ denote the closures of these manifolds.

Theorem 2.18

Each two of the following statements are equivalent:
(a) $\bar{K} = C[0,1]$,
(b) the infinite series

$$\sum_{p=0}^{\infty} \left(1 - \left| \frac{\sqrt{1 + k_p} - 1}{\sqrt{1 + k_p} + 1} \right| \right)$$

diverges,
(c) if φ is a *real*-valued and normalized function of bounded variation on $[0,1]$ such that

$$\int_0^1 (1 + k_p t)^{-1} \, d\varphi(t) = 0, \qquad p = 0,1,\ldots,$$

then $\varphi \equiv 0$,
(d) $\mathbf{1} \in \bar{K}$, where $\mathbf{1}$ denotes the function $f \in C[0,1]$ such that $f(t) \equiv 1$,
(e) $\bar{K}_p = L_p(0,1)$ for $1 \leq p < \infty$, and
(f) $\mathbf{1} \in \bar{K}_p$ for some p such that $1 \leq p < \infty$.

Proof. The transformation $z = 4x(1 - x)^{-2}$ maps the domain $|x| < 1$ upon the domain $\text{ext}[-\infty, -1]$, and has the inverse

$$x = [(1 + z)^{1/2} - 1][(1 + z)^{1/2} + 1]^{-1},$$

where that branch of $(1 + z)^{1/2}$ is taken which is 1 for $z = 0$. Condition (b) asserts that $\sum_{p=0}^\infty (1 - |x_p|)$ is divergent where

$$x_p = [(1 + k_p)^{1/2} - 1][(1 + k_p)^{1/2} + 1]^{-1}.$$

Each term of the sequence $\{H_n(x)\}_{n=0}^{\infty}$, where

$$H_n(x) = \prod_{p=0}^{n} \left[\frac{x_p - x}{1 - \bar{x}_p x} \frac{\bar{x}_p - x}{1 - x_p x} \right] \tag{2.18a}$$

is analytic and has modulus less than 1 on $|x| < 1$, and if $-1 < x < 1$, then the sequence is nondecreasing. It follows, [cf. Theorem 1.3; the function $H_n(x) = B_n(x) \cdot B_n(\bar{x})$] that the sequence $\{H_n(x)\}_{n=0}^{\infty}$ converges to a function H which has modulus less than 1, is real for real x, and is different from the identically zero function if and only if the series $\Sigma_{p=0}^{\infty}(1 - |x_p|)$ is convergent. It follows from Corollary 2.3.1 that

$$H(x) = \sqrt{1 + z} \int_0^1 (1 + zt)^{-1} d\sigma(t) \tag{2.18b}$$

where $z = 4x(1 - x)^{-2}$ and σ is a real-valued and normalized function of bounded variation which is uniquely determined by H. Hence, if $\bar{K} = C[0,1]$, then (2.18b) shows that $H \equiv 0$ and the series (b) is divergent; i.e., (a) implies (b).

If λ is a normalized function of bounded variation such that

$$\int_0^1 (1 + k_p t)^{-1} d\lambda(t) = 0, \qquad p = 0,1,\ldots,$$

$\lambda(t) = [\lambda_1(t) - \lambda_2(t)] + i[\lambda_3(t) - \lambda_4(t)]$, where λ_j is nondecreasing and

$$F(4x(1 - x)^{-2}) = \sqrt{1 + z} \int_0^1 (1 + zt)^{-1} d\lambda(t),$$

then $F(4x(1 - x)^{-2})$ is a linear combination of functions with positive real part (cf. Theorem 2.3) and, therefore, is the ratio of two bounded analytic functions (cf. proof of Theorem 1.6.2). That is, $F(4x(1 - x)^{-2})$ is beschränktartige (Theorem 2.6) and consequently $L(F,1) < \infty$. Hence, (b) implies (a).

Obviously (a) implies (c). The argument used in establishing (2.18b) shows (c) implies (b) and, therefore, (c) implies (a). Clearly (a) implies (d). Suppose now that $f_n(t) = \Sigma_{p=0}^{n} c_{pn}(1 + k_p t)^{-1}$ and f_n converges to $\mathbf{1}$ uniformly on $[0,1]$. For each positive integer $s \leq n$ let L_{ns} denote $\Sigma_{p=0}^{n} c_{pn} k_p^{-s}$.

Then

$$\sum_{p=0}^{n} c_{pn}k_p^{-s}(1 + k_p t)^{-1}$$

$$= L_{ns} - tL_{ns-1} + \cdots + (-t)^{s-1}L_{n1} + (-t)^s f_n(t).$$

In particular, if $s = 1$, then

$$tf_n(t) = L_{n1} - \sum_{p=0}^{n} c_{pn}(1 + k_p t)^{-1}k_p^{-1}.$$

If $\varepsilon > 0$, then there exists $N > 0$ such that if $n > N$ and $0 \le t \le 1$, then the right-hand member of this expression differs from t by less than $\varepsilon/2$. There exists $M > 0$ such that if $m > M$ and $0 \le t \le 1$, then $L_{n1} f(t)$ differs from L_{n1} by less than $\varepsilon/2$. Hence

$$\left| t + [f_n(t) - f_m(t)] \right| = \left| [t - tf_n(t)] + [L_{n1} - f_m(t)] \right| < \varepsilon,$$

so that $t \in \overline{K}$. We now see, by mathematical induction, that $t^s \in \overline{K}$ for $s = 0, 1, \ldots$. It follows from the Weierstrass polynomial theorem (cf. Corollary 1.15.1) that $C[0,1] = \overline{K}$ and, therefore, (d) implies (a).

Obviously (a) implies (e). Suppose now that (e) holds and (b) does not. Let $F(z) = [H(4z(1 - z)^{-2})][(1 + z)^{1/2}][1 + (1 + z)^{1/2}]^{-2}$, where $H(x)$ is the function of (2.18b). In accordance with Corollary 2.3.1,

$$F(z) = \sqrt{1 + z} \int_0^1 (1 + zt)\, d\sigma(t) \qquad (2.18c)$$

where σ is a real-valued and normalized function of bounded variation on $[0,1]$. We need to show that σ is absolutely continuous and $\sigma' \in L_q(0,1)$, $1 < q \le \infty$. A simple computation gives $\left| t^{-1}I_m F(-(1/t) + iy) \right| \le 1$, so that (2.4a) of Theorem 2.4 shows σ is absolutely continuous. Similarly, (2.4b) of Theorem 2.4 shows $\left| \sigma'(t) \right| \le \pi$. Hence $\sigma' \in L_p^*(0,1)$ and (e) implies (b) which, in turn, implies (a).

The argument that (e) and (f) are equivalent is similar to the argument showing (a) and (d) are equivalent. This completes the proof of Theorem 2.18.

There are many consequences of Theorem 2.18 and we shall discuss a few. However, before doing this we shall give an example to show that (c) is not a simple consequence of the Riesz representation theorem.

Example 2.18. Suppose $f_p(t) = (1 - t)t^p + it(1 - t)^p$, $p = 0, 1, \ldots$. The assumption that $\sum_{p=0}^{n} c_{pn}f_p(t) \to 1$ as $n \to \infty$ gives, for $t = 0$ and $t = 1$, the incompatible relations $c_{on} \to 1$ and $c_{on} \to i$, so that **1** is not in the closed linear manifold generated by $\{f_p\}_{p=0}^{\infty}$ in $C[0,1]$ and, consequently, $\{f_p\}_{p=0}^{\infty}$ is not fundamental in $C[0,1]$. On the other hand, if φ is a real-valued and normalized function of bounded variation on $[0,1]$ such that

$$\int_0^1 f_p(t)\, d\varphi(t) = 0, \qquad p = 0,1,\ldots,$$

then

$$\int_0^1 t^p\, d\varphi(t) = 0, \qquad p = 0,1,\ldots,$$

and (cf. Theorem 1.15) $\varphi \equiv 0$; i.e., (c) is a property not shared by other families in $C[0,1]$. For a deeper insight along these lines, the reader is referred to the paper of Bohnenblust and Sobczyk [6].

Corollary 2.18.1

In order that $\{(1 + k_p t)^{-1}\}_{p=0}^{\infty}$ be fundamental in $C[0,1]$ or $L_p(0,1)$, $1 \le p < \infty$, it is necessary that the infinite series $\Sigma_{p=0}^{\infty} |k_p|^{-1/2}$ be divergent.

Proof. Suppose that $\Sigma_{p=0}^{\infty} |k_p|^{-1/2} < \infty$. Then

$$|x_p| = |1 - \lambda(\sqrt{1 + k_p} + 1)^{-1}| \ge 1 - \lambda|(1 + k_p)^{1/2} + 1|$$

and $\Pi_{p=0}^{\infty} |x_p| > 0$. Hence, $\Pi_{p=0}^{\infty} (1 - (1 - |x_p|)) > 0$ and $\Sigma_{p=0}^{\infty} (1 - |x_p|) < \infty$.

The necessary condition of the last corollary is also a sufficient condition under additional restrictions on k_p.

Corollary 2.18.2

Suppose $0 < \theta < \pi$, $\delta > 0$, $|\arg(1 + k_p)| \le \theta$ for $p = 0,1,\ldots,$ and $|1 + k_p| \ge \delta$ for $p = 0,1,\ldots$. Then a necessary and sufficient condition in order that $\{(1 + k_p t)^{-1}\}_{p=0}^{\infty}$ be fundamental in $C[0,1]$ is that the infinite series $\Sigma_{p=0}^{\infty} |k_p|^{-1/2}$ be divergent.

Proof. Note that the conditions on the argument and modulus of $(1 + k_p)$ require that k_p be outside an infinite keyhole that is symmetric about the ray $[-\infty, -1]$. The necessity of the condition follows from the previous corollary. Suppose now $\Sigma_{p=0}^{\infty} |k_p|^{-1/2}$ diverges and $(1 + k_p) = r_p^2 e^{i2\theta} p$. Then

$$|x_p|^2 = 1 - r_p^{-1} \frac{4r_p^2 \cos \theta_p}{1 + 2r_p \cos \theta_p + r_p^2}.$$

Our hypothesis implies $\Sigma_{p=0}^{\infty} r_p^{-1} = \infty$ and, consequently, $\Pi_{p=0}^{\infty} |x_p| = 0$. From (b) of Theorem 2.18, this implies $\overline{K} = C[0,1]$.

Corresponding to (c) of Theorem 2.18 we have that if f is real-valued and $f \in L_q(0,1)$, $1 < q \le \infty$, and

$$\int_0^1 (1 + k_n t)^{-1} f(t) \, dt = 0, \qquad n = 0,1,\ldots,$$

then either $f(t) = 0$ a.e. or $\overline{K}_p = L_p(0,1)$, where $p^{-1} + q^{-1} = 1$. (d) and (f) can be extended so that, say, $P \in \overline{K}$ implies $\overline{K} = C[0,1]$, where P is a polynomial. To see this suppose $P(t) = t^s + a_{s-1}t^{s-1} + \cdots + a_0$ and

$$f_n(t) = \sum_{p=0}^{n} c_{pn}(1 + k_p t)^{-1} \to P(t)$$

as $n \to \infty$. Then

$$P(t) - f_n(t) = \frac{Q_1(t)}{\Pi_{p=0}^{n}(1 + k_p t)} = \frac{Q(t)}{\Pi_{p=0}^{n}(k_p^{-1} + t)} \qquad (2.18d)$$

where $Q(t)$ is a polynomial of degree $n + s + 1$. If $\{h_j\}_{j=1}^{s}$ is a set of distinct numbers in $(0,1)$ and each h_j is distinct from every k_p, then, by partial fractions,

$$\frac{Q(t)}{\Pi_{j=1}^{s}(h_j^{-1} + t)\Pi_{p=0}^{n}(k_p^{-1} + t)} = 1 - \sum_{j=1}^{s} b_{jn}(1 + h_j t)^{-1} - \sum_{p=0}^{n} d_{pn}(1 + k_p t)^{-1}.$$

$$(2.18e)$$

Comparing (2.18d) with (2.18e) we have

$$\left| 1 - \sum_{j=1}^{s} b_{jn}(1 + h_j t)^{-1} - \sum_{p=0}^{n}(1 + k_p t)^{-1} \right| \le |P(t) - f_n(t)| \to 0$$

as $n \to \infty$. Hence, by (d) and (b) of Theorem 2.18, we have

$$\sum_{p=-s}^{\infty} \left(1 - \left| \frac{(1 + k_p)^{1/2} - 1}{(1 + k_p)^{1/2} + 1} \right| \right) = \infty,$$

where $k_{-p} = h_p$ for $p = 1,\ldots,s$. This implies the divergence of

$$\sum_{p=0}^{\infty} \left(1 - \left| \frac{(1 + k_p)^{1/2} - 1}{(1 + k_p)^{1/2} + 1} \right| \right),$$

which, in turn, implies $\overline{K} = C[0,1]$.

We shall deviate from our main theme of relating analytic function theory with approximation theory and probe deeper into the nature of approximating with the rational functions described in Theorem 2.18. More precisely, we shall show that the problem of approximating with this set of rational functions is a complicated problem in interpolation theory. Our point of departure for this probe is (d) of Theorem 2.18. Suppose, therefore, that $f_n(t) = \Sigma_{p=0}^n c_{pn}(1 + k_p t)^{-1}$ and $|1 - f_n(t)| \to 0$ as $n \to \infty$ and $0 \le t \le 1$. Then

$$1 - f_n(t) = \frac{Q_n(t)}{\Pi_{p=0}^n (1 + k_p t)}$$

where Q_n is a polynomial of degree $n + 1$. If we ignore multiple roots for the time being, then there exists $n + 1$ points t_{jn}, $j = 0,1,\ldots,n + 1$, such that $Q_n(t_{jn}) = 0$, or, what is the same, $f_n(t_{jn}) = 1$ for $j = 0,1,\ldots,n + 1$. That is, the numbers c_{pn} determine the numbers t_{jn}, and, conversely, if the numbers t_{jn} are given in advance, then they uniquely determine the numbers c_{pn}.

In other words, the problem of determining the c_{pn} so that $|1 - f_n(t)| \to 0$ as $n \to \infty$ is a problem of judiciously selecting the interpolating points t_{jn}. This is a complicated problem. For example, if $|k_p| > e^{-1}$ for all p and the t_{jn} are selected in the most obvious way, $t_{jn} = j/n$, $j = 0,1,\ldots,n$, then $1 - f_n(j/n) = 0$ and $f_n(1/2n) = 0(8^n)$; i.e., the curve $f_n(t)$ humps badly at the point $1/2n$. This is remedied by crowding all the interpolation points near the origin and, so to speak, pull the hump down, which, in turn and again so to speak, snaps the curve $f_n(t)$ into almost a straight line.

We shall make the above statements more precise in the form of a sequence of lemmas and theorems. The lemmas basically evolve from solving the linear system of equation

$$\sum_{p=0}^n c_{pn}(1 + k_p t_p)^{-1} = 1$$

for the unknowns c_{pn}. Also, as a matter of convenience we consider $(k_p^{-1} + t)^{-1}$ in place of $(1 + k_p t)^{-1}$.

Lemma 2.19.1

If n is a positive integer, $\{x_p\}_{p=0}^n$ a sequence of numbers such that $x_p \neq x_q$ for $p \neq q$ ($p,q = 0,1,\ldots,n$),

$$\pi_p^{(n)} = \prod_{\substack{i=0 \\ i \neq p}}^n (x_p - x_i)^{-1},$$

$S_m^{(0)} = 1$ for $m = 0,1,\ldots$, and, for each positive integer p,

$$S_n^{(p)} = \sum_{i=0}^{n} x_i S_i^{(p-1)}, \qquad n = 0,1,\ldots,$$

then

$$\sum_{p=0}^{n} \pi_p^{(n)} x_p^r = \begin{cases} 0, & r = 0,1,\ldots, n-1 \\ S_n^{(m)}, & r = n+m, m = 0,1,\ldots. \end{cases} \qquad (2.19a)$$

Proof. If r is a nonnegative integer less than n, then

$$\frac{x^r}{(x-x_1)(x-x_2)\cdots(x-x_n)} = \sum_{j=1}^{n} \frac{A_j}{x-x_j}$$

where $A_j = \pi_j^{(n)}(x_j - x_0)x_j^r$, $j = 1,2,\ldots, n$. The first part of formula (2.19a) for $r = 0,1,\ldots, n-1$ results from putting $x = x_0$ in the above partial-fraction expansion. Since

$$S_1^{(m)} = \frac{x_0^{1+m} - x_1^{1+m}}{x_0 - x_1},$$

the second part of the formula is true in the case $n = 1$. If n is greater than 1 and m is nonnegative, then, by induction,

$$\sum_{p=0}^{n} \pi_p^{(n)} x_p^{n+m} = \sum_{p=0}^{n-1} \pi_p^{(n-1)} x_p^{n-1+m} \left[1 + \frac{x_n}{x_p - x_n} \right] + \pi_n^{(n)} x_n^{n+m}$$

$$= \begin{cases} S_{n-1}^{(m)} + x_n S_n^{(m-1)} = S_n^{(m)} & \text{if } m > 0 \\ S_{n-1}^{(0)} = S_n^{(0)} & \text{if } m = 0. \end{cases}$$

Lemma 2.19.2

If $\{\varepsilon_i^{(n)}\}_{i=0}^{n}$ is a sequence of numbers, $c_p^{(n)} = \pi_p^{(n)} \prod_{i=0}^{n}(x_p + \varepsilon_i^{(n)})$, and $c_p^{(n)} \neq 0$ for $p = 0,1,\ldots, n$, then the function

$$f_n^{(0)}(x) = \sum_{p=0}^{n} \frac{c_p^{(n)}}{x + x_p}$$

has the property $f_n^{(0)}(\varepsilon_i^{(n)}) = 1$, $i = 0,1,\ldots, n$.

Proof. By (2.19a),

$$f_n^{(0)}(\varepsilon_i^{(n)}) = \sum_{p=0}^{n} \pi_p^{(n)}(x_p + \varepsilon_s^{(n)}) = 1$$

for $i = 0,1,\ldots, n$.

Lemma 2.19.3

Under the hypothesis of Lemma 2.19.2 and the additional hypothesis $\varepsilon_0^{(n)} = 0$,

$$f_n^{(0)}(x) = 1 - \prod_{i=0}^{n} \frac{(x - \varepsilon_i^{(n)})}{x + x_i}. \tag{2.19b}$$

Proof

$$\frac{\prod_{i=1}^{n}(x - \varepsilon_i^{(n)})}{\prod_{i=0}^{n}(x + x_i)} = \sum_{j=0}^{n} \frac{A_j}{x + x_j},$$

where

$$A_j = \frac{\prod_{i=1}^{n}(-x_j - \varepsilon_i^{(n)})}{\prod_{i=0,i \neq j}^{n}(-x_j + x_i)} = \pi_j^{(n)} \prod_{i=1}^{n}(x_j + \varepsilon_i^{(n)}).$$

Therefore,

$$1 - \prod_{i=0}^{n} \frac{x - \varepsilon_i^{(n)}}{x + x_i} = 1 - x \sum_{p=0}^{n} \frac{c_p^{(n)}}{x_p(x + x_p)}$$

$$= 1 - \sum_{p=0}^{n} c_p^{(n)} \left[1 - \frac{x_p}{x + x_p} \right] \frac{1}{x_p}$$

$$= 1 - \sum_{p=0}^{n} c_p^{(n)} x_p^{-1} + f_n^{(0)}(x) = f_n^{(0)}(x).$$

Lemma 2.19.4

If r is a nonnegative integer and the hypothesis of Lemma 2.19.2 holds, then the function

$$F_n^{(r)}(x) = \sum_{p=0}^{n} \frac{c_p^{(n)} x_p^r}{x + x_p}$$

is

$$\sum_{p=0}^{n} c_p^{(n)} x_p^{r-1} - x \sum_{p=0}^{n} c_p^{(n)} x_p^{r-2} + \cdots + (-x)^{r-1} \sum_{p=0}^{n} c_p^{(n)} + (-x)^r f_n^{(0)}(x).$$

Proof. This follows immediately upon multiplying each member of the identity

$$\frac{1}{x + x_p} = \sum_{i=0}^{r-1} \frac{(-x)^i}{x_p^{i+1}} + \frac{(-x)^r}{x_p^r(x + x_p)}$$

by $c_p^{(n)} x_p^r$ and summing over p from 0 to n.

If we set

$$\prod_{i=0}^{n} (x + \varepsilon_i^{(n)}) = x^{n+1} + a_{n1}x^{n-1} + \cdots + a_{nn}x + a_{n,n+1},$$

$a_{np} = 0$ if $p > n + 1$, then it follows from (2.19a) that

$$\sum_{p=0}^{n} c_p^{(n)}x_p^s = S_n^{(s+1)} + a_{n1}S_n^{(s)} + \cdots + a_{ns}S_n^{(1)} + a_{n,n+1}S_n^{(0)}. \quad (2.19c)$$

If we denote this last expression by $T_n^{(s-1)}$, then the formula of Lemma 2.19.4 may be written

$$F_n^{(r)}(x) = T_n^{(r)} - xT_n^{(r-1)} + \cdots + (-x)^{r-1}T_n^{(1)} + (-x)^r f_n^{(0)}(x),$$
$$T_n^{(s)} = S_n^{(s)} + a_{n1}S_n^{(s-1)} + \cdots + a_{n,s-1}S_n^{(1)} + a_{ns}S_n^{(0)}, \quad (2.19d)$$
$$S_n^{(s)} = S_{n-1}^{(s)} + x_n S_n^{(s-1)}.$$

If we set

$$\Delta^0 S_n^{(s)} = S_n^{(s)}, \Delta^1 S_n^{(s)} = \frac{\Delta^0 S_n^{(s)} - \Delta^0 S_{n-1}^{(s)}}{x_n},$$

$$\Delta^2 S_n^{(s)} = \frac{\Delta^1 S_n^{(s)} - \Delta^1 S_{n-1}^{(s)}}{x_n}, \ldots,$$

then

$$T_n^{(s)} = \sum_{i=0}^{s} a_{ni}\Delta^i S_n^{(s)}, \qquad a_{no} = 1. \quad (2.19e)$$

With this notation,

$$T_n^{(r)} = \sum_{i=0}^{r} a_{ni}\Delta^i S_n^{(r)},$$

$$T_n^{(r-1)} = \sum_{i=0}^{r-1} a_{ni}\Delta^{i+1} S_n^{(r)},$$
$$\vdots$$
$$T_n^{(1)} = \sum_{i=0}^{1} a_{ni}\Delta^{i-1} S_n^{(r)},$$

and consequently,

$$F_n^{(r)}(x) = \sum_{j=0}^{r-1} (-x)^i \sum_{j=0}^{r-1} a_{nj}\Delta^{j+1} S_n^{(r)} + (-x)^r f_n^{(0)}(x). \quad (2.19f)$$

Theorem 2.19

If $\{x_i\}_{i=0}^{\infty}$ is a sequence of numbers each different from zero, $x_i \neq x_j$ if $i \neq j$ $(i,j = 0,1,\ldots)$, $R_e x_j \geq 0$ $(j = 0,1,\ldots)$, and the series

$$\sum_{p=0}^{\infty} [R_e(x_p) + \{I_m(x_p)\}^2]$$

diverges, then the sequence $\{(x_p + x)^{-1}\}_{p=0}^{\infty}$ is fundamental on each bounded subset of the nonnegative numbers. That is, if B is a bounded subset of the nonnegative numbers, f a continuous function on $0 \leq x < \infty$, and $\varepsilon > 0$, then there exists a sequence $\{A_p\}_{p=0}^{n}$ of numbers such that if $x \in B$

$$\left| \sum_{p=0}^{n} A_p(x_p + x)^{-1} - f(x) \right| < \varepsilon.$$

Proof. In view of (2.19d), it will suffice to prove that $f_n^{(0)}(x) \to 1$ as $n \to \infty$, uniformly over each bounded subset of the nonnegative numbers. We set $m_n = \text{g.l.b.}[|x_0|, |x_1|, \ldots, |x_n|]$ and $\varepsilon_i^{(n)} = (i/n)m_n$. By (2.19b),

$$\left| f_n^{(0)}(x) - 1 \right| = \prod_{i=0}^{n} \frac{|x - \varepsilon_i^{(n)}|}{|x + x_i|}.$$

Let M be a number such that if $x \in B$, then $x \leq M$. If p is a nonnegative integer less than n and $(p/n)m_n \leq x \leq (p + 1/n)m_n$, then

$$\prod_{i=0}^{n} |x - \varepsilon_i^{(n)}| = x(x - \varepsilon_1^{(n)})(x - \varepsilon_2^{(n)}) \cdots (x - \varepsilon_p^{(n)})(\varepsilon_{p+1}^{(n)} - x) \cdots (\varepsilon_n^{(n)} - x)$$

$$\leq \varepsilon_{p+1}^{(n)}(\varepsilon_{p+1}^{(n)} - \varepsilon_1^{(n)}) \cdots (\varepsilon_{p+1}^{(n)} - \varepsilon_p^{(n)})(\varepsilon_{p+1}^{(n)} - \varepsilon_p^{(n)}) \cdots (\varepsilon_n^{(n)} - \varepsilon_p^{(n)})$$

$$\leq \frac{m_n^{n+1}}{\binom{n}{p}} \frac{n!}{n^{n+1}}.$$

Also, $\Pi_{i=0}^{n} |x + x_i| \geq \Pi_{i=0}^{n} |x_i| \geq m_n^{(n)}$; therefore (Sterling's formula)

$$\left| f_n^{(0)}(x) - 1 \right| \leq \frac{n!}{n^{n+1}} < \frac{C}{e^n n^{1/2}}$$

where C is a positive number. If $m_n < x$, then

$$\left| f_n^{(0)}(x) - 1 \right| \leq \frac{x^{n+1}}{\Pi_{i=0}^{n} |x + x_i|} = \prod_{i=0}^{n} \left| 1 + \frac{x}{x_i} \right|^{-1}$$

$$= \prod_{i=0}^{n} [\{1 + x^{-1}R_e(x_i)\}^2 + \{x^{-1}I_m(x_i)\}^2]^{-1/2}$$

$$\leq \prod_{i=0}^{n} [\{1 + M^{-1}R_e(x_i)\}^2 + \{M^{-1}I_m(x_i)\}^2]^{-1/2}.$$

If $\varepsilon > 0$, then there exists $N > 0$ such that if $n > N$, then the last expression is less than $\varepsilon/2$ and $Ce^{-n}n^{-1/2}$. Hence

$$\left| f_n^{(0)}(x) - 1 \right| < \varepsilon.$$

Theorem 2.20

If in addition to the hypothesis of Theorem 2.19, $x_p > 0$, $m_n = 0(1/n)$, $\varepsilon_i^{(n)} = (i/n)m_n$, r a nonnegative integer, and $\{c_p^{(n,r)}\}_{p=0}^n$ are numbers such that if

$$f_n^{(r)}(x) = \sum_{p=0}^n \frac{c_p^{(n,r)}}{x + x_p},$$

then $f_n^{(r)}(\varepsilon_i^{(n)}) = (\varepsilon_i^{(n)})^r$ and $f_n^{(r)}(x) \to x^r$ uniformly over each bounded subset of the nonnegative numbers.

Proof

$$\sum_{i=0}^n |a_{ni}| \leq \prod_{i=1}^n (1 + \varepsilon_i^{(n)}) < [(1 + m_n)^{-m_n}]^{nm_n} < e^{nm_n}$$

and $(\Sigma_{i=0}^n |x_i|)^r < C^r n^r$, where C is a positive number, and, therefore, $S_n^{(p)}| \leq C^p n^p$. From (2.19f) we find that

$$x^r[f_n^{(0)}(x)]^{r+1} = \begin{vmatrix} F_n^{(0)}(x) & f_n^{(0)}(x) & 0 & 0 & \cdots & 0 \\ F_n^{(1)}(x) & T_n^{(1)} & f_n^{(0)}(x) & 0 & \cdots & 0 \\ \vdots & \vdots & \vdots & & & \vdots \\ & & & & & f_n^{(1)}(x) \\ F_n^{(r)}(x) & T_n^{(r)} & \cdots & & & T_n^{(1)} \end{vmatrix}$$

and therefore the function $f_n^{(r)}(x)$ is given by

$$f_n^{(r)}(x) = \begin{vmatrix} F_n^{(0)}(x) & 1 & 0 & & \cdots & 0 \\ F_n^{(1)}(x) & T_n^{(1)} & 1 & & \cdots & 0 \\ F_n^{(2)}(x) & T_n^{(2)} & T_n^{(1)} & 0 & \cdots & 0 \\ \vdots & \vdots & \vdots & & & \vdots \\ & & & & & 0 \\ & & & & & 1 \\ F_n^{(r)}(x) & T_n^{(r)} & T_n^{(r-1)} & & \cdots & T_n^{(1)} \end{vmatrix}.$$

Consequently,

$$x^r[f_n^{(0)}(x)]^{r+1} - f_n^{(r)}(x) = [f_n^{(0)}(x) - 1]W_n^{(r)}(x)$$

where $W_n^{(r)}(x) = 0(ne^{nm_n})^q$ and q is a positive integer. Therefore if $0 \leq x \leq m_n$,

$$|x^r[f_n^{(0)}(x)]^{r+1} - f_n^{(r)}(x)| = 0\left[\frac{n^q e^{nqm_n}}{e^n n^{1/2}}\right].$$

Since $m_n \to 0$ as $n \to \infty$, if $\varepsilon > 0$ there exists $N > 0$ such that the left-hand member of the least expression is less than $\varepsilon/2$ for $n > N$. If $m_n < x \le M$, then,

$$\left| x^r [f_n^{(0)}(x)]^{r+1} - f_n^{(r)}(x)] \right| = 0\left[\frac{(\sum_{p=0}^n |x_p|)^q}{C^{1/2M}(\sum_{p=0}^n |x_p|)} \right]$$

so that, taking N still larger if necessary, this will be less than $\varepsilon/2$ for $n > N$.

Example. The crucial step in the use of these interpolating methods is the evaluation of the numbers $S_n^{(p)}$. For certain choices of x_p, this evaluation can be rather simple. For example, if $x_p = (p + 1)^{-1}$, then

$$S_n^{(p)} = [(n + 1)/p!] \int_0^1 x^n [-\log(1 - x)]^p \, dx.$$

For additional details concerning the closure properties of these functions see [69], [70], [65], [21], [84], [85], and [91].

Chapter 3

BOUNDARY VALUES AND
H_p SPACES

IN THIS CHAPTER we shall introduce the H_p spaces of analytic functions and study some of the geometry of these spaces and their relationship to the L_p spaces. Our point of departure for this is (2.1a).

Theorem 3.1

If φ is real-valued and of bounded variation on $[0,2\pi]$ and f is analytic on $|x| < 1$ such that

$$f(x) = \frac{1}{2\pi} \int_0^{2\pi} \frac{e^{it} + x}{e^{it} - x} \, d\varphi(t), \tag{3.1a}$$

then $\lim_{r \to 1} R_e f(re^{it}) = \varphi'(t)$ a.e.

Proof. The proof is analogous to the proof of Lemma 1.63. From (3.1a) we have

$$R_e f(re^{i\theta}) = \frac{1}{2\pi} \int_0^{2\pi} \frac{1 - r^2}{1 - 2r\cos(\theta - t) + r^2} \, d\varphi(t).$$

Suppose $0 < t_0 < 2\pi$, $\varphi'(t_0)$ exists, and

$$\varphi(t) = \varphi(t_0) + (t - t_0)\varphi'(t_0) + (t - t_0)h(t),$$

so that h is bounded on $[0,2\pi]$, $h(t_0) = 0$, and h is continuous at $t = t_0$. Hence

$$R_e f(re^{it_0}) = \varphi'(t_0) + \frac{1}{2\pi} \int_0^{2\pi} \frac{1 - r^2}{1 - 2r\cos(t_0 - t) + r^2} \, d\{(t - t_0)h(t)\}.$$

58

Now

$$\frac{1}{2\pi} \int_0^{2\pi} \frac{1 - r^2}{1 - 2r \cos(t_0 - t) + r^2} \, d\{(t - t_0)h(t)\}$$

$$= -\frac{1}{2\pi} \int_0^{2\pi} (t - t_0)h(t) \, d\left\{\frac{1 - r^2}{1 - 2r \cos(t_0 - t) + r^2}\right\}$$

$$+ \frac{1}{2\pi} \frac{1 - r^2}{1 - 2r \cos(t_0) + r^2} \{(2\pi - t_0)h(2\pi) + t_0 h(0)\}.$$

Inasmuch as h is a bounded function on $[0, 2\pi]$ and $0 < t_0 < 2\pi$, the last term in the above equation goes to zero as r goes to 1. Suppose now $\varepsilon > 0$, $\delta > 0$, and $|h(t)| < \varepsilon$ for $|t - t_0| < \delta$. Then

$$I(r) = \left| \frac{1}{2\pi} \int_{t_0 - \delta}^{t_0 + \delta} (t - t_0)h(t) \, d\left\{\frac{1 - r^2}{1 - 2r \cos(t_0 - t) + r^2}\right\} \right|,$$

or

$$(2r)^{-1}I_r \leq \frac{\varepsilon}{2\pi} \int_{t_0 - \delta}^{t_0 + \delta} \frac{(t_0 - t)(1 - r^2) \sin(t_0 - t)}{(1 - 2r \cos(t_0 - t) + r^2)^2} \, dt$$

$$\leq \frac{\varepsilon}{2\pi} \int_{t_0 - \delta}^{t_0 + \delta} \frac{1 - r^2}{1 - 2r \cos(t_0 - t) + r^2} \, dt + \frac{\varepsilon \delta \sin \delta(1 - r^2)}{4\pi r \sin^2(\delta/2)}$$

$$\leq \frac{\varepsilon}{2\pi} \int_0^{2\pi} \frac{1 - r^2}{1 - 2r \cos(t_0 - t) + r^2} \, dt + \frac{\varepsilon \delta \sin \delta(1 - r^2)}{4\pi r \sin^2(\delta/2)}.$$

Hence $\lim_r \sup I(r) < \varepsilon$. Finally, if $|h(t)| \leq M$ for $0 \leq t \leq 2\pi$ and

$$\left| \frac{(t_0 - t) \sin(t_0 - t)}{(1 - 2r \cos(t_0 - t) + r^2)^2} \right| \leq N$$

for $0 \leq t \leq t_0 - \delta$ or $t_0 + \delta \leq t \leq 2\pi$, then

$$\frac{(1 - r)^2}{2\pi} \left| \int_0^{t_0 - \delta} \frac{(t_0 - t) \sin(t_0 - t)}{(1 - 2r \cos(t_0 - t) + r^2)^2} \, dt \right.$$

$$+ \left. \int_{t_0 + \delta}^{2\pi} \frac{(t_0 - t) \sin(t_0 - t)}{(1 - 2r \cos(t_0 - t)^2 + r^2)^2} \, dt \right| \leq (1 - r^2)NM.$$

This concludes the proof of Theorem 3.1.

The following is a basic theorem due to F. and M. Riesz [77].

Theorem 3.2

If f is analytic and bounded on $|x| < 1$, then $\lim_{r \to 1} f(re^{i\theta})$ exists a.e. for $0 \le \theta \le 2\pi$.

Proof. Suppose $|f(x)| \le M$ for $|x| < 1$ and set $h(x) = f(x) - I_m f(0)$. Then $h(x) = 2M - (2M - h(x))$ and, in accordance with Theorem 2.1, each of the functions $2M$ and $2M - h(x)$ can be represented in the form (3.1a). It follows from Theorem 3.1 that $\lim_{r \to 1} R_e f(re^{i\theta})$ exists. Applying the same consideration to the function if (x) gives $\lim_{r \to 1} I_m f(re^{i\theta})$ exists a.e.

Combining Theorems 2.6 and 3.2 gives us

Corollary 3.2.1

If f is analytic and beschränktartige on $|x| < 1$, then $\lim_{r \to 1} f(re^{i\theta})$ exists a.e. (cf. [59], p. 190).

Theorem 3.3

Suppose that α is a complex number, E a subset of $[0,2\pi]$ having positive Lebesgue measure, f analytic and bounded on $|x| < 1$, and $\lim_{r \to 1} f(re^{i\theta}) = \alpha$ for $\theta \in E$. Then $f(x) \equiv \alpha$.

Proof. The function $h(x) = f(x) - \alpha$ is bounded on $|x| < 1$ and $\lim_{r \to 1} h(re^{i\theta}) = 0$ for $\theta \in E$. Suppose $|h(x)| \le M$. In accordance with Corollary 1.5.2, if m is the smallest nonnegative integer such that $h^{(m)}(0) \ne 0$, then

$$\log \left| \frac{h^{(m)}(0)}{Mm!} \right| \le L(M^{-1}h, r).$$

However, our hypothesis implies $L(M^{-1}h, r) \to -\infty$ as $r \to 1$.

Theorems 2.6 and 3.3 yield

Corollary 3.3.1

If α is a complex number, E a subset of $[0,2\pi]$ with positive Lebesgue measure, $f(x)$ analytic and beschränktartige on $[0,2\pi]$, and $\lim_{r \to 1} f(re^{i\theta}) = \alpha$ for $\theta \in E$, then $f(x) \equiv \alpha$ (cf. [59], p. 197).

Definition 3.1. If $0 < p < \infty$ and f is analytic on $|x| < 1$, then the number $M_p(f,r)$ is defined by

$$M_p(f,r) = \left\{ \frac{1}{2\pi} \int_0^\infty |f(re^{i\theta})|^p \, d\theta \right\}^{1/p}.$$

Theorem 3.4

If f is analytic on $|x| < 1, 0 < p < \infty$, and $0 < r_1 < r_2 < 1$, then $M_p(f,r_1) \le M_p(f,r_2)$.

Proof. Suppose h is analytic on $|x| < 1$ and

$$h(x) = \sum_{p-0}^\infty a_p x^p.$$

Then

$$\frac{1}{2\pi} \int_0^{2\pi} |h(re^{i\theta})|^2 \, d\theta = \sum_{p=0}^\infty |a_p|^2 r^{2p} = [M_2(f,r)]^2.$$

Hence, for such a function $M_2(h,r_1) \le M_2(h,r_2)$, and if, in addition,

$$\left\{ \frac{1}{2\pi} \int_0^{2\pi} |h(re^{i\theta})|^2 \, d\theta \right\}^{1/2}$$

is bounded above, independent of r, then

$$\lim_{r \to 1} M_2(h,r) = \left(\sum_{p=0}^\infty |a_p|^2 \right)^{1/2} < \infty ;$$

in this situation we denote $(\sum_{p=0}^\infty |a_p|^2)^{1/2}$ by $M_2(f,1)$.

Returning to the hypothesis of the theorem, we set $g(x) = f(r_2 x)$ so that $g = BF$ (cf. Corollary 1.5.1), where B is a finite Blaschke product, F is analytic and zero-free on $|x| < 1$, and F is continuous on $|x| \le 1$. Hence

$$M_p(g,r) = M_p(BF,r) \le M_p(F,r). \tag{3.1b}$$

However,

$$[M_p(F,r)]^p = [M_2(F^{p/2},r)]^2 \le [M_2(F^{p/2},1)]^2 = [M_p(F,1)]^p,$$

where the symbol $M_p(F,1)$ is defined by the last equation. Comparing the last expression with (3.1b) gives us

$$M_p(g,r) \le M_p(F,1) = M_p(g,1), \tag{3.1c}$$

where

$$M_p(g,1) = \left\{ \frac{1}{2\pi} \int\limits_0^{2\pi} |g(e^{i\theta})|^p \, d\theta \right\}^{1/p}$$

and makes sense since g is continuous on $|x| \leq 1$. If we now select r so that $r_1 = rr_2$, (3.1b) gives us

$$M_p(f,r_1) = M_p(f,rr_2) = M_p(g,r) \leq M_p(g,1) = M_p(f,r_2).$$

Definition 3.2. If f is analytic on $|x| < 1$ and $0 < p < \infty$, then f belongs to $H_p(0,2\pi)$ if and only if $\lim_{r \to 1} M_p(f,r)$ exists; whenever this limit exists we denote it by $M_p(f,1)$. If $p = \infty$, then f belongs to $H_\infty(0,2\pi)$ if and only if $\sup_{|x|<1} |f(x)| < \infty$; we denote this sup by $M_\infty(f)$.

The spaces $H_p(0,2\pi)$ go back to Hardy [25] and Riesz [75] and have always fascinated mathematicians. For a modern and elegant treatment of these spaces together with many applications, see [98] and [37]. We leave it as an exercise for the reader to show that $f \in H_\infty(0,2\pi)$ if and only if $f \in H_p(0,2\pi)$, uniformly in p, and in such a case, $M_\infty(f) = \lim_p M_p(f,1)$.

Theorem 3.5
If f is analytic on $|x| < 1$, $0 < p \leq \infty$, and $f \in H_p(0,2\pi)$, then $f = Bh$ and $M_p(f,1) = M_p(h,1)$, where h is zero-free on $|x| < 1$ and B is the Blaschke product of the zeros of f.

Proof. Since

$$\frac{1}{2\pi} \int\limits_0^{2\pi} \log|f(re^{i\theta})| \, d\theta \leq \frac{1}{p} \frac{1}{2\pi} \int\limits_0^{2\pi} |f(re^{i\theta})|^p \, d\theta \leq \frac{1}{p}[M_p(f,1)]^p,$$

$L(f,1) < \infty$, by Theorem 1.5, $f = Bh$. Since $|f(x)| \leq |h(x)|$ for $|x| < 1$, $M_p(f,r) \leq M_p(h,r)$. Now for $0 < r < 1$ and $\varepsilon < 0$ there exists $n_0 > 0$ such that $n > n_0$ implies

$$|h(re^{i\theta})| = \frac{|f(re^{i\theta})|}{|B(re^{i\theta})|} \leq (1 + \varepsilon)\frac{|f(re^{i\theta})|}{|B_n(re^{i\theta})|}$$

where B_n is the nth partial product used in defining B and (recall)

$$\lim_{|x| \to 1} |B_n(x)| = 1.$$

Hence

$$M_p(h,r) \leq (1 + \varepsilon)M_p\left(\frac{f}{B_n},r\right) \leq (1 + \varepsilon)M_p\left(\frac{f}{B_n},1\right) = (1 + \varepsilon)M_p(f,1),$$

or, what is the same, $M_p(h,r) \leq M_p(f,1)$, so that $M_p(h,1)$ exists and $M_p(h,1) = M_p(f,1)$. In case $p = \infty$, then

$$\max_{|x| < r} |h(x)| \leq (1 + \varepsilon) \max_{|x| = r} \left| \frac{f(x)}{B_n(x)} \right| \leq (1 + \varepsilon) \lim_{r \to 1} \max_{|x| = r} |f(x)|.$$

This together with $|f(x)| \leq |h(x)|$ shows that $M_\infty(f) = M_\infty(h)$ and completes the proof of Theorem 3.5.

Suppose that f belongs to $H_p(0,2\pi)$, $p > 0$. Then

$$L^+(f,r) \leq p^{-1}[M_p(f,r)]^p \leq p^{-1}[M_p(f,1)]^p$$

and, therefore, f is beschränktartige. This is of sufficient interest to be stated as

Theorem 3.6

If $0 < p$ and f is analytic on $|x| < 1$ such that f belongs to $H_p(0,2\pi)$, then f is beschränktartige.

Theorem 3.7

If $\{x_p\}_{p=1}^\infty$ is a sequence of numbers such that $|x_p| < 1$ for $p = 1,2,\ldots$, $\Sigma_{p=1}^\infty (1 - |x_p|)$ is convergent, and B the Blaschke product constructed from $\{x_p\}_{p=1}^\infty$, then $\lim_{r \to 1} |B(re^{i\theta})| = 1$ a.e.

Proof. Set $B(e^{i\theta}) = \lim_{r \to 1} B(re^{i\theta})$. In view of Theorem 3.2, this limit exists a.e. and by the Lebesgue bounded convergence theorem $B(e^{i\theta})$ is integrable. Since $|B(x)| \leq 1$, it follows from Fatou's lemma that

$$0 \leq \frac{1}{2\pi} \int_0^{2\pi} - \log|B(e^{i\theta})| \, d\theta \leq \liminf_{r \to 1} \frac{1}{2\pi} \int_0^{2\pi} - \log|B(re^{i\theta})| \, d\theta.$$

From Theorem 1—4 we get

$$\liminf_{r \to 1} \frac{1}{2\pi} \int_0^{2\pi} \log|B(re^{i\theta})| \, d\theta = \lim_{r \to 1} L(B,r) = 0.$$

This implies $\log|B(e^{i\theta})| = 0$ a.e., or, what is the same, $|B(e^{i\theta})| = 1$ a.e.

Theorem 3.8

If $0 < p < \infty$ and f belongs to $H_p(0,2\pi)$, then there exists a unique function F in $L_p(0,2\pi)$ such that
(1) $\lim_{r \to 1} f(re^{i\theta}) = F(\theta)$ a.e.,

(2) $\lim\limits_{r \to 1} \int\limits_{0}^{2\pi} |f(re^{i\theta}) - F(\theta)|^p \, d\theta = 0$, and

(3) $M_p(f,1) = \left\{ \dfrac{1}{2\pi} \int\limits_{0}^{2\pi} |F(\theta)|^p \, d\theta \right\}^{1/p}$.

Proof. It follows from Theorem 3.6 and Corollary 3.3.1 that $\lim_{r \to 1} f(re^{i\theta})$ exists a.e. We denote the limit by $F(\theta)$, and it follows from Fatou's lemma that $|F|^p$ is integrable and $\{(1/2\pi) \int_0^{2\pi} |F(\theta)|^p \, d\theta\}^p \le M_p(f,1)$. We shall first prove the theorem for several special cases.

Case 1. $p = 2$. This is immediate inasmuch as $M_2(f,r) = \{\Sigma_{p=0}^{\infty} |a_j|^2 r^{2j}\}^{1/2}$, where $f(x) = \Sigma_{j=0}^{\infty} a_j x^j$.

Case 2. $p = 1$ and f is zero-free. In this situation $f^{1/2}$ is analytic on $|x| < 1$ and belongs to $H_2(0,2\pi)$. Hence, if $0 < r < r_1 < 1$,

$$\frac{1}{2\pi} \int\limits_{0}^{2\pi} |f(re^{i\theta}) - f(r_1 e^{i\theta})| \, d\theta = \frac{1}{2\pi} \int\limits_{0}^{2\pi} |f^{1/2}(re^{i\theta}) - f^{1/2}(r_1 e^{i\theta})|$$

$$|f^{1/2}(re^{i\theta}) + f^{1/2}(r_1 e^{i\theta})| \, d\theta$$

$$\le \left\{ \frac{1}{2\pi} \int\limits_{0}^{2\pi} |f^{1/2}(re^{i\theta}) - f^{1/2}(r_1 e^{i\theta})|^2 \, d\theta \right\}^{1/2}$$

$$\times \left\{ \frac{1}{2\pi} \int\limits_{0}^{2\pi} |f^{1/2}(re^{i\theta}) + f^{1/2}(r_1 e^{i\theta})|^2 \, d\theta \right\}^{1/2}.$$

It follows from case 1 that

$$\lim\limits_{r \to 1} \left\{ \frac{1}{2\pi} \int |f^{1/2}(re^{i\theta}) - f^{1/2}(r_1 e^{i\theta})|^2 \, d\theta \right\}^{1/2} = 0.$$

From the Minkowski inequality we get

$$\left\{ \frac{1}{2\pi} \int\limits_{0}^{2\pi} |f^{1/2}(re^{i\theta}) + f^{1/2}(r_1 e^{i\theta})|^2 \, d\theta \right\}^{1/2} \le 2[M_1(f^1,1)]^2.$$

Inasmuch as $\lim_{r \to 1} f(re^{i\theta}) = F(\theta)$ and $\{f(re^{i\theta})\}_{r<1}$ is Cauchy in the L_1 norm, the theorem follows readily in case $p = 1$ and f is zero-free.

Case 3. $1 < p$ and f is zero-free. In this case f^p is analytic, belongs to $H_1(0,2\pi)$, and $[M_p(f,1)]^p = M_1(f^p,1)$. Suppose $E' \subset [0,2\pi]$ and is measurable; then from case 2, we get

$$\lim_{r \to 1} \int_{E'} |f(re^{i\theta})|^p \, d\theta = \int_{E'} |F(\theta)|^p \, d\theta.$$

Suppose now that $\varepsilon > 0$ and $\delta > 0$. By Egoroff's theorem (!) there exist $r_0 > 0$ and $E \supset [0,2\pi]$ such that E is measurable, E has Lebesgue measure greater than $2\pi - \delta$, and for $r > r_0$, $r_1 > r_0$, and $\theta \in E$ we have

$$|f(re^{i\theta}) - f(r_1e^{i\theta})|^p < \varepsilon.$$

Hence, if $E' = [0,2\pi] - E$,

$$\int_0^{2\pi} |f(re^{i\theta}) - f(r_1e^{i\theta})|^p \, d\theta = \int_E |f(re^{i\theta}) - f(r_1e^{i\theta})|^p \, d\theta$$

$$+ \int_{E'} |f(re^{i\theta}) - f(r_1e^{i\theta})|^p \, d\theta$$

$$\leq \varepsilon 2\pi + \left[\left\{ \int_{E'} |f(re^{i\theta})|^p \, d\theta \right\}^{1/p} \right.$$

$$\left. + \left\{ \int_{E'} |f(r_1e^{i\theta})|^p \, d\theta \right\}^{1/p} \right]^p,$$

where the term in the bracket comes from applying Minkowski's inequality to the last term in the middle of the above expression. Consequently,

$$\lim_{r_1,r \to 1} \int_0^{2\pi} |f(re^{i\theta}) - f(r_1e^{i\theta})|^p \, d\theta \leq \varepsilon 2\pi + 2^p \int_{E'} |F(e^{i\theta})|^p \, d\theta.$$

Since $|F(e^{i\theta})|^p$ belongs to $L_1(0,2\pi)$, the integral

$$\int_0^\theta |F(e^{i\varphi})|^p \, d\varphi$$

defines an absolutely continuous function on $[0,2\pi]$ and we can select δ so that

$$\int_{E'} |F(e^{i\theta})|^p \, d\theta < \varepsilon.$$

Case 4. $0 < p < 1$ and $f(x)$ is zero-free. In this case $f^{1/2}$ is analytic on $|x| < 1$ and belongs to $H_{2p}(0,2\pi)$. Hence, for $0 < r < r_1 < 1$,

$$\int_0^{2\pi} |f(re^{i\theta}) - f(r_1 e^{i\theta})|^p \, d\theta \le \int_0^{2\pi} |f^{1/2}(re^{i\theta}) - f^{1/2}(r_1 e^{i\theta})|^p$$

$$\times |f^{1/2}(re^{i\theta}) + f^{1/2}(re^{i\theta})|^p \, d\theta$$

$$\le \left\{ \int_0^{2\pi} |f^{1/2}(re^{i\theta}) - f^{1/2}(r_1 e^{i\theta})|^{2p} \, d\theta \right\}^{1/2}$$

$$\times \left\{ \int_0^{2\pi} |f^{1/2}(re^{i\theta}) + f^{1/2}(r_1 e^{i\theta})|^{2p} \, d\theta \right\}^{1/2},$$

$$\left\{ \int_0^{2\pi} |f^{1/2}(re^{i\theta}) + f^{1/2}(r_1 e^{i\theta})|^{2p} \, d\theta \right\}^{1/2} \le \left\{ \int_0^{2\pi} |f(re^{i\theta})|^p \, d\theta \right\}^{1/2}$$

$$+ \left\{ \int_0^{2\pi} |f(r_1 e^{i\theta})|^p \, d\theta \right\}^{1/2}$$

$$\le 2[\{M_p(f,1)\}^p]^{1/2}.$$

If we denote $2[\{M_p(f,1)\}^p]^{1/2}$ by N, then

$$\int_0^{2\pi} |d(re^{i\theta}) - f(r_1 e^{i\theta})|^p \, d\theta \le N \left\{ \int_0^{2\pi} |f^{1/2}(re^{i\theta}) - f^{1/2}(re^{i\theta})|^{2p} \, d\theta \right\}^{1/2}.$$

From case 3 we have that the above expression goes to zero as $r \to 1$ if $2p > 1$ or $p > \frac{1}{2}$, so that the zero-free case holds for $p > \frac{1}{2}$. Hence, the above expression goes to zero if $2p > \frac{1}{2}$ or $p > \frac{1}{4}$, etc. (cf. [97]).

Case 5. $0 < p$ and f may have zeros. In this case we have $f = Bh$, where, in accordance with Theorem 3.5, h belongs to $H_p(0,2\pi)$ and $M_p(f,1) = M_p(h,1)$. If $r < r_1 < 1$, then

$$\left\{ \int_0^{2\pi} |f(re^{i\theta}) - f(r_1 e^{i\theta})|^p \, d\theta \right\}^{1/p} \le \delta \left\{ \int_0^{2\pi} |B(re^{i\theta})|^p |h(re^{i\theta}) - h(r_1 e^{i\theta})|^p \, d\theta \right\}^{1/p}$$

$$+ \delta \left\{ \int_0^{2\pi} |h(r_1 e^{i\theta})|^p |B(re^{i\theta}) - B(r_1 e^{i\theta})|^p \, d\theta \right\}^{1/p},$$

where $\delta = 2^{(1-p)/p}$ or $\delta = 1$ according as to $0 < p < 1$ or $1 \le p$. Inasmuch as we have proved the theorem for the zero-free case, we have, since $|B(x)| < 1$,

$$\int_0^{2\pi} |B(re^{i\theta})|^p |h(re^{i\theta}) - h(r_1 e^{i\theta})|^p \, d\theta \le \int_0^{2\pi} |h(re^{i\theta}) - h(r_1 e^{i\theta})|^p \, d\theta$$

and the last expression goes to zero as $r \to 1$. Also, if we denote $\lim_{r \to 1} h(re^{i\theta})$ by $h(\theta)$, then

$$\int_0^{2\pi} |h(r_1 e^{i\theta})|^p |B(re^{i\theta}) - B(r_1 e^{i\theta})|^p \, d\theta \leq 2^p \int_0^{2\pi} |h(r_1 e^{i\theta}) - h(e^{i\theta})|^p \, d\theta$$

$$+ \int_0^{2\pi} |h(e^{i\theta})|^p |B(re^{i\theta}) - B(r_1 e^{i\theta})|^p \, d\theta.$$

Again the second integral goes to zero as $r_1 \to 1$. Finally,

$$|h(e^{i\theta})|^p |B(re^{i\theta}) - B(r_1 e^{i\theta})|^p \leq 2^p |h(e^{i\theta})|^p.$$

Since $|h(e^{i\theta})|^p$ belongs to $L_1(0,2\pi)$, Theorem 3.7 with the Lebesgue-dominated convergence theorem gives us

$$\lim_{r \to 1} \int_0^{2\pi} |h(e^{i\theta})|^p |B(re^{i\theta}) - B(r_1 e^{i\theta})|^p \, d\theta = 0.$$

This completes the proof of Theorem 3.8. We shall need the following corollary, which is a consequence of the proof of Theorem 3.8.

Corollary 3.8.1

Suppose f is analytic on $|x| < 1$ and belongs to $H_1(0,2\pi)$, $0 < r < 1$,

$$\varphi_r(\theta) = \frac{1}{2\pi} \int_0^\theta f(re^{it}) \, dt,$$

and $\varphi_r(0) = 0$. Then $\{\varphi_r\}_{r<1}$ is a family of uniformly absolutely continuous functions. That is, for $\varepsilon > 0$ there exists $\delta > 0$ such that if $\{[a_p,b_p]\}_{p \geq 1}$ is family of pairwise-disjoint subintervals of $[0,2\pi]$ satisfying $\Sigma_p(b_p - a_p) < \delta$, then $\Sigma_{p \geq 0} |\varphi_r(b_p) - \varphi_r(a_p)| < \varepsilon$ for every r.

Proof. In accordance with Theorem 3.8 there exists F in $L_1(0,2\pi)$ such that $\lim_{r \to 1} f(re^{i\theta}) = F(\theta)$. Set $\varphi(\theta) = (1/2\pi) \int_0^\theta F(t) \, dt$. φ is absolutely continuous, so that for $\varepsilon > 0$ there exists $\delta_1 > 0$ such that $\Sigma_p |\varphi(b_p) - \varphi(a_p)| < \varepsilon/2$ whenever $\Sigma_p |b_p - a_p| < \delta_1$ and $\{[a_p,b_p]\}_{p \geq 1}$ are pairwise-disjoint. From (2) of Theorem 3.8, there exists $r_0 < 1$ such that $\int_0^{2\pi} |f(re^{i\theta}) - F(\theta)| \, d\theta < \varepsilon/2$ for $r > r_0$. Hence, for $r > r_0$,

$$\sum_p |\varphi_r(b_p) - \varphi_r(a_p)| \leq \sum_p |\varphi(b_p) - \varphi(a_p)| + \sum_p |\{\varphi_r(b_p) - \varphi(b_p)\} - \{\varphi_r(a_p) - \varphi(a_p)\}|$$

$$\leq \frac{\varepsilon}{2} + \frac{1}{2\pi} \int_0^{2\pi} |f(re^{i\theta}) - F(\theta)| \, d\theta < \varepsilon.$$

For $0 < r \le r_0$, let M denote $\max_{|x| \le r_0} |f(x)|$. Hence, $\delta = \min(\delta_1, \varepsilon M^{-1})$ is the required δ.

Corollary 3.8.2
  If $1 \le p \le \infty$, then $H_p(0,2\pi)$ is a Banach space where the norm is $\|f\|_p = M_p(f,1)$, $1 \le p < \infty$, and $\|f\|_\infty = M_\infty(f)$.

The proof of this corollary is left to the reader. We note that if $1 \le p < \infty$, then $H_p(0,2\pi)$ is separable, whereas $H_\infty(0,2\pi)$ is not separable (cf. [87], p. 93).
  For $1 \le p < \infty$ and $F \in L_p(0,2\pi)$, then we define

$$\|F\|_p = \left\{ \frac{1}{2\pi} \int\limits_0^{2\pi} |F(t)|^p \, dt \right\}^{1/p}.$$

The factor $(2\pi)^{-1}$ is a normalizing factor inserted for convenience. Note for $F \in L_p(0,2\pi)$,

$$\|F\|_p = \sup_{\|G\|_q = 1} \frac{1}{2\pi} \int\limits_0^{2\pi} F(t)\overline{G(t)} \, dt$$

since $L_p^*(0,2\pi) = L_q(0,2\pi)$, $p^{-1} + q^{-1} = 1$.
  The following theorem due to F. Riesz is fundamental to the H_p theory. It has been significantly generalized by Bochner [4], Helson and Lowdenslager [31], and Masani and Wiener [50]; in this connection see [78], pp. 193ff. We have decided not to give these elegant proofs in order to present a proof that easily extends to the case of the real line (cf. Theorem A of Appendix A).

Theorem 3.9
  Suppose φ is a normalized function of bounded variation of $[0,2\pi]$ such that

$$\int\limits_0^{2\pi} e^{in\theta} \, d\varphi(\theta) = 0$$

for $n = 1,2,\ldots$. Then (1) φ is absolutely continuous, and (2) there exists uniquely an analytic function k on $|x| < 1$ such that $k \in H_1(0,2\pi)$ and $\lim_{r \to 1} k(re^{i\theta}) = \varphi'(\theta)$ a.e.

Proof. Set

$$\alpha_p = \frac{1}{2\pi} \int\limits_0^{2\pi} e^{-ip\theta} \, d\varphi(\theta), \qquad p = 0,1,\ldots \tag{3.9a}$$

and

$$k(x) = \sum_{p=0}^{\infty} \alpha_p x^p = \frac{1}{2\pi} \int_0^{2\pi} \frac{1}{1 - xe^{-i\theta}} \, d\varphi(\theta). \tag{3.9b}$$

Inasmuch as $R_e(1 - xe^{-i\theta})^{-1} > 0$ for $|x| < 1$, we see that $k(x)$ is a linear combination of functions with positive real part so that (cf. the proof of Theorem 1.6.2) k is the ratio of two bounded functions and, as a consequence of Theorem 2.6, k is beschränktartige. It follows from Corollary 3.2.1 that $\lim_{r\to 1} k(re^{i\theta})$ exists a.e.[1] Since

$$(1 - xe^{-i\theta})^{-1} = 2^{-1}(e^{i\theta} + x)(e^{i\theta} - x)^{-1} + 2^{-1},$$

we have

$$2k(x) = \frac{1}{2\pi} \int_0^{2\pi} \frac{e^{i\theta} + x}{e^{i\theta} - x} \, d\varphi(\theta) + \alpha,$$

where $\alpha = (2\pi)^{-1}\varphi(2\pi)$. Let $\varphi = \varphi_0 + i\varphi_1$ and

$$k_j(x) = \frac{1}{2\pi} \int_0^{2\pi} \frac{1}{1 - x_j e^{i\theta}} \, d\varphi_j(\theta) - (2\pi)^{-1}\varphi_j(2\pi) \qquad j = 0,1.$$

Hence, $k_j(0) = 0$ and our hypothesis implies

$$\int_0^{2\pi} e^{-ip\theta} \, d\varphi_0(\theta) = i \int_0^{2\pi} e^{-ip\theta} \, d\varphi_1(\theta),$$

so that $R_e k_0 = I_m k_1$ and $I_m k_0 = R_e k_1$. Inasmuch as

$$R_e k_j(re^{i\theta}) + (2\pi)^{-1}\varphi_j(2\pi) = \frac{1}{2\pi} \int_0^{2\pi} \frac{1 - r^2}{1 - 2r\cos(\theta - t) + r^2} \, d\varphi_j(t),$$

we have (cf. the proof of Theorem 3.1)

$$\lim_{r\to 1} \{R_e k_j(re^{i\theta}) + (2\pi)^{-1}\varphi_j(2\pi)\} = \varphi_j'(\theta) \quad \text{a.e.}$$

Hence

$$\lim_{r\to 1} k_0(re^{i\theta}) = \lim_{r\to 1} \{R_e k_0(re^{i\theta}) + iR_e k_1(re^{i\theta})\}$$

$$= \varphi'(\theta) - (2\pi)^{-1}\varphi(2\pi) \quad \text{a.e.}$$

and

$$\lim_{r\to 1} k_1(re^{i\theta}) = \lim_{r\to 1} \{R_e k_1(re^{i\theta}) - iR_e k_0(re^{i\theta})\}$$

$$= -i\varphi'(\theta) + i(2\pi)^{-1}\varphi(2\pi) \quad \text{a.e.}$$

---

[1] At this point we can show that the measures $\int k(e^{i\theta})d\theta$ and $d\varphi$ have the same Fourier–Stieltjes transform and complete the proof using the uniqueness of the Fourier–Stieltjes transform.

Since $k = k_1 + ik_2 + \alpha$, we have

$$\lim_{r \to 1} k(re^{i\theta}) = 2\varphi'(\theta) - \alpha \quad \text{a.e.}$$

We must show that φ is absolutely continuous. To this end, if we set

$$\varphi_r(\theta) = \frac{1}{2\pi} \int_0^\theta R_e\{2k(re^{it}) - \varphi(2\pi)\},$$

then $\varphi_r(\theta) \to \varphi(\theta)$ as $r \to 1$. The proof of Corollary 3.8.1 shows that $\{\varphi_r\}_{r<1}$ is a uniformly absolutely continuous family of functions. Hence φ is absolutely continuous. The uniqueness of k follows from (3.9a) and (3.9b).

This completes the proof of Theorem 3.9.

The following question seems to be a natural question to ask and may give some insight into the complexities of Theorem 3.9. Suppose φ is a normalized function of bounded variation on $[0,2\pi]$ and f belongs to $H_1(0,2\pi)$ such that $f(re^{i\theta}) \to \varphi'(\theta)$ a.e., then is φ absolutely continuous? The answer is no and to see this take φ to be a simple step function and $f \equiv 0$.

Theorem 3.10

If $1 \le p \le \infty$ and $F \in L_p(0,2\pi)$, then the following statements are equivalent:

(1) $\displaystyle\int_0^{2\pi} e^{in\theta} F(\theta)\, d\theta = 0 \qquad n = 1,2,\ldots,$

(2) there exists a function f on $|x| < 1$ such that $f \in H_p(0,2\pi)$,

and

$$\lim_{r \to 1} f(re^{i\theta}) = F(\theta) \quad \text{a.e.},$$

$$\lim_{r \to 1} \int_0^{2\pi} |f(re^{i\theta}) - F(\theta)|^p\, d\theta = 0.$$

Proof. In view of Theorem 3.8, (2) clearly implies (1). Suppose (1) holds and we set

$$\varphi(\theta) = \int_0^\theta F(t)\, dt$$

and $\varphi(0) = 0$. Then $\varphi'(\theta) = F(\theta)$ a.e. and Theorem 3.9 shows that there exists an analytic function f on $|x| < 1$ such that $f \in H_1(0,2\pi)$ and $f(re^{i\theta}) \to F(\theta)$ a.e. Theorem 3.8 shows that

$$\lim_{r \to 1} \int_0^{2\pi} |f(re^{i\theta}) - F(\theta)|\, d\theta = 0.$$

Suppose $p > 1$, $p^{-1} + q^{-1} = 1$, and $0 < r < r_1 < 1$. Poisson's formula gives us

$$f(re^{i\theta}) = \lim_{r_1 \to 1} \frac{1}{2\pi} \int_0^{2\pi} \frac{r_1^2 - r^2}{r_1^2 - 2r_1 r \cos(\theta - t) + r^2} f(r_1 e^{it}) \, dt$$

$$= \frac{1}{2\pi} \int_0^{2\pi} \frac{1 - r^2}{1 - 2r \cos(\theta - t) + r^2} F(t) \, dt.$$

If we have $P(r,\theta,t) = (1 - r^2)(1 - 2r \cos(\theta - t) + r^2)^{-1}$, then

$$|f(re^{i\theta})|^p \leq \left\{ \frac{1}{2\pi} \int_0^{2\pi} [P(r,\theta,t)]^{1/q} [P(r,\theta,t)]^{1/p} |F(t)| \, dt \right\}^p$$

$$\leq \left\{ \frac{1}{2\pi} \int_0^{2\pi} P(r,\theta,t) \, dt \right\}^{p/q} \left\{ \frac{1}{2\pi} \int_0^{2\pi} P(r,\theta,t) |F(t)|^p \, dt \right\}$$

$$= \frac{1}{2\pi} \int_0^{2\pi} P(r,\theta,t) |F(t)|^p \, dt.$$

If we integrate $|f(re^{i\theta})|^p$ with respect to θ and use the Fubini theorem, we get

$$\frac{1}{2\pi} \int_0^{2\pi} |f(re^{i\theta})|^p \, d\theta \leq \frac{1}{2\pi} \int_0^{2\pi} |F(e^{it})|^p \left\{ \frac{1}{2\pi} \int_0^{2\pi} P(r,\theta,t) \, d\theta \right\} dt$$

$$= \frac{1}{2\pi} \int_0^{2\pi} |F(e^{it})|^p \, dt.$$

Hence $M_p(f,r) \leq \|F\|_p$, $f \in H_p(0,2\pi)$, and, by Theorem 3.8,

$$\lim_{r \to 1} \int_0^{2\pi} |f(re^{i\theta}) - F(\theta)|^p \, d\theta = 0.$$

The case $p = \infty$ is left to the reader.

If $F \in L_p(0,2\pi)$, $p \geq 1$, then

$$a_n = \frac{1}{2\pi} \int_0^{2\pi} e^{-int} F(t) \, dt$$

exists for $n = 0, \pm 1, \ldots$, and, consequently, F has the formal Fourier-series expansion

$$F(t) \cong \sum_{n=-\infty}^{\infty} a_n e^{int}.$$

This series gives rise to the function

$$f(x) = \sum_{n=0}^{\infty} a_n x^n,$$

which is analytic on $|x| < 1$. f is called the *analytic part* of F.

If, for a given p, we define the function T_p on $L_p(0,2\pi)$, so that $T_p(F) = f$, f the analytic part of F, then T_p is a linear and homogeneous function on $L_p(0,\infty)$. In case $1 < p < \infty$, T_p will turn out to be a bounded function from $L_p(0,2\pi)$ to $H_p(0,2\pi)$ and we shall use this to characterize the dual space of $H_p(0,2\pi)$. The proof that T_p is bounded for $1 < p < \infty$ is not easy.

We shall need the following lemma due to Calderon [11]. The proof of the lemma is left to the reader.

Lemma 3.11.1

If $1 < p < \infty$, $p \neq 3,5,7,\ldots$, and $|\theta| < \pi/2$, then there exists numbers α and β such that

$$|\sin \theta|^p \le 1 \le \alpha \cos p\theta + \beta(\cos \theta)^p. \tag{3.11a}$$

We now come to the theorem of M. Riesz [76]; see also [98].

Theorem 3.11

If $1 < p < \infty$, $F \in L_p(0,2\pi)$, and

$$g(x) = \frac{1}{2\pi} \int_0^{2\pi} \frac{e^{it} + x}{e^{it} - x} F(t)\, dt,$$

then $g \in H_p(0,2\pi)$ and there exists $K_p > 0$ such that $M_p(g,1) \le K_p\|F\|_p$; moreover, K_p depends only on p and is independent of F.

Proof. First let us note that

$$g(x) = 2f(x) + \frac{1}{2\pi} \int_0^{2\pi} F(t)\, dt$$

where f is the analytic part of F. Hence, Theorem 3.11 implies $M_p(f,1) \le K_p'\|F\|_p$, where $K_p' = 2^{-1}(K_p + 1)$. Without loss of generality we may assume $F \ge 0$. Therefore,

$$g(re^{i\theta}) = \frac{1}{2\pi} \int_0^{2\pi} \frac{1 - r^2}{1 - 2r\cos(\theta - t) + r^2} F(t)\, dt$$

$$+ \frac{i}{2\pi} \int_0^{2\pi} \frac{2r\sin(\theta - t)}{1 - 2r\cos(\theta - t) + r^2} F(t)\, dt.$$

Set $g(re^{i\theta}) = u(re^{i\theta}) + iv(re^{i\theta})$, where u and v are defined by the last equation. Our hypothesis that $F \geq 0$ implies $u(re^{i\theta}) \geq 0$ and, in fact, $u(re^{i\theta}) > 0$ unless $F \equiv 0$. Proceeding exactly as in the proof of Theorem 3.10, we have

$$\frac{1}{2\pi} \int_0^{2\pi} |u(re^{i\theta})|^p \, d\theta \leq (\|F\|_p)^p. \tag{3.11b}$$

If $F \not\equiv 0$ (in the contrary case the theorem is trivial), then $u > 0$ and $g(x) \neq 0$ for $|x| < 1$. Hence, $[g(x)]^p = [u(x) + iv(x)]^p$ is well defined and analytic on $|x| < 1$ and $g(0) = u(0)$. Upon applying Poisson's formula to the analytic function $[g]^p$, we get

$$[u(0)]^p = \frac{1}{2\pi} \int_0^{2\pi} [u(re^{i\theta}) + iv(re^{i\theta})]^p \, d\theta$$

$$= \left\{ \frac{1}{2\pi} \int_0^{2\pi} u(re^{i\theta}) \, d\theta \right\}^p \tag{3.11c}$$

where the last equality comes from applying Poisson's formula to the harmonic function $u(re^{i\theta})$. Also, we have

$$R_e[u(x) + iv(x)]^p = [u^2(x) + v^2(x)]^{p/2} \cos \arg(u(x) + iv(x))^p$$

$$= [u^2(x) + v^2(x)]^{p/2} \cos p \arg(u(x) + iv(x)). \tag{3.11d}$$

Since $u(x) > 0$, $-\pi/2 < \arg(u(x) + iv(x)) < \pi/2$. Assuming $p \neq 3, 5, 7, \ldots$, using (3.11a) with $\theta = \arg(u(x) + iv(x))$ and multiplying (3.11a) by $[u^2(x) + v^2(x)]^{p/2}$ gives us

$$(u^2 + v^2)^{p/2} \leq \alpha(u^2 + v^2)^{p/2} \cos p \arg(u + iv)$$

$$+ \beta(u^2 + v^2)^{p/2} [\cos \arg(u + iv)]^p. \tag{3.11e}$$

Also,

$$(u^2 + v^2)^{p/2} [\cos \arg(u + iv)]^p = [|g| \cos \arg g]^p = u^p.$$

Hence

$$\frac{\beta}{2\pi} \int_0^{2\pi} (u^2 + v^2)^{p/2} [\cos \arg(u + iv)]^p = \frac{\beta}{2\pi} \int_0^{2\pi} [u(re^{i\theta})]^p \, d\theta. \tag{3.11f}$$

Using (3.11d) to obtain the real part of (3.11c) yields

$$\frac{1}{2\pi} \int_0^{2\pi} [u^2 + v^2]^{p/2} \cos p \arg(u + iv) = [u(0)]^p = \left\{ \frac{1}{2\pi} \int_0^{2\pi} u(re^{i\theta}) \, d\theta \right\}. \tag{3.11g}$$

Combining (3.11e), (3.11f), and (3.11g) gives

$$\frac{1}{2\pi} \int_0^{2\pi} [u^2(re^{i\theta}) + v^2(re^{i\theta})]^{p/2}\, d\theta = \frac{\beta}{2\pi} \int_0^{2\pi} [u(re^{i\theta})]^p\, d\theta + |\alpha| \left\{ \frac{1}{2\pi} \int_0^{2\pi} u(re^{i\theta})\, d\theta \right\}^p,$$

or, using Holder's inequality and (3.11b),

$$\frac{1}{2\pi} \int_0^{2\pi} |g(re^{i\theta})|^p\, d\theta \le \frac{\beta}{2\pi} \int_0^{2\pi} |u(re^{i\theta})|^p\, d\theta + \frac{|\alpha|}{2\pi} \int_0^{2\pi} |u(re^{i\theta})|^p\, d\theta$$

$$\le (\beta + |\alpha|) \|F\|_p.$$

Hence, for these choices of p, $K_p \le (\beta + |\alpha|)$ and depends only on p and $M_p(f,1) \le K_p'\|F\|_p$, where $K_p' = \inf[m;\, M_p(f,1) \le m\|F\|_p]$.

We now go to the special values $p = 3,5,7,\ldots$, and shall show that the case $2 \le p < \infty$ can be obtained from the case $1 < p \le 2$. In our proof we use the fact that functions of the form

$$\sum_{|n| < \infty N} a_n e^{in\theta}$$

are dense in every $L_p(0,2\pi)$, $p < \infty$ (cf. Corollary 2.1.1); these functions are called *trigonometric polynomials*. Suppose that $2 \le q < \infty$ and $p^{-1} + q^{-1} = 1$, so that $1 < p \le 2$. Let

$$F_1(t) = \sum_{|n| < \infty} a_n e^{int}$$

and

$$F_2(t) = \sum_{|n| < \infty} b_n e^{int}$$

be trigonometric polynomials and f_1 and f_2 their respective analytic parts. By using the definition of norm in a dual space of a Banach space and allowing F_2 to roam over all trigonometric polynomials with $\|F_2\|_p = 1$,

$$M_q(f_1,1) = \|f_1\|_q = \sup_{\|F_2\|_p = 1} \left| \frac{1}{2\pi} \int_0^{2\pi} f_1(e^{it})\overline{F_2(t)}\, dt \right|$$

$$= \sup_{\|F_2\|_q = 1} \left| \frac{1}{2\pi} \int_0^{2\pi} |f_2(e^{-it})F_1(t)\, dt \right|$$

$$\le \|F_1\|_q \sup_{\|F_2\|_q = 1} \left\{ \frac{1}{2\pi} \int_0^{2\pi} |f_2(e^{it})|^p\, dt \right\}^p$$

$$\le K_p'\|F_1\|_q.$$

Hence, taking $K'_p = K'_q$, the theorem is true for any $F \in L_q(0,2\pi)$ such that F is a trigonometric polynomial. Suppose now $F(t) \cong \Sigma^\infty_{n=-\infty} a_n e^{int}$, $F_m(t) = \Sigma^m_{n=-m} a_{nm} e^{int}$, and $\|F - F_m\|_q \to 0$ as $m \to \infty$. Then $\|F_m - F_{m'}\| \to 0$ and $M_q(f_m - f'_m, 1) \le K'_p \|F_m - F_{m'}\| \to 0$ as $m,m' \to \infty$. Inasmuch as $H_q(0,2\pi)$ is a Banach space (Corollary 3.8.2), there exists $h \in H_q(0,2\pi)$ such that $M_q(h - f_m, 1) \to 0$ as $m \to \infty$ and $M_q(h,1) \le K'_q \|F\|_q$. Clearly,

$$h(x) = \sum_{n=0}^\infty a_n x^n$$

is the analytic part of F.

This concludes the proof of Theorem 3.11. Following Theorem 3.19 we shall give an example to show that Theorem 3.11 fails for $p = 1$ and $p = \infty$.

Recalling the remarks in the paragraph immediately preceding Lemma 3.11.1, we have proved that $M_p(T_p F, 1) \le \|T_p\| \cdot \|F\|_p$ and $\|T_q\| = \|T_p\|$ for $1 < p < \infty$ and $p^{-1} + q^{-1} = 1$.

We need to digress to refine Corollary 2.1.1; i.e., we shall make a finer development of the closure properties of the sets $\{e^{ij\theta}\}^\infty_{j=-\infty}$ and $\{x^j\}^\infty_{j=0}$ in the spaces $L_p(0,2\pi)$ and $H_p(0,2\pi)$. Our presentation follows the one given by Zygmund (cf. [98]).

Theorem 3.12a

If $1 < p < \infty$, $F \in L_p(0,2\pi)$, $F(t) \cong \Sigma^\infty_{n=-\infty} a_n e^{int}$, h the analytic part of F, and $h_m(x) = \Sigma^m_{n=0} a_n e^{int}$, then $M_p(h - h_m, 1) \le (K'_p)^2 \|F\|_p$.

Proof. Let $f_m(x) = x^{-m}[h(x) - h_m(x)]$. Then $M_p(h,1) \le K'_p \|F\|_p$ and

$$f_m(x) = \frac{1}{2\pi} \int_0^{2\pi} \frac{e^{imt} h(e^{it})}{1 - xe^{it}} \, dt$$

so that $f_m(x)$ is the analytic part of $e^{imt} h(e^{it})$ and, by Theorem 3.11, $M_p(f_m,1) \le K'_p M_p(h,1)$. Consequently,

$$M_p(h - h_m, 1) = M_p(f_m, 1) \le (K'_p)^2 \|F\|_p.$$

Theorem 3.12b

If $1 < p < \infty$, $f \in H_p(0,2\pi)$, $f_m(x) = \Sigma^m_{n=0} a_n x^n$, $m = 0,1,\ldots$, then

$$M_p(f - f_m, 1) \to 0$$

as $m \to \infty$.

Proof. Inasmuch as x^j is the analytic part of e^{ijt}, $j = 0,1,\ldots$, we have from Corollary 2.1.1 and Theorem 3.11 that $\{x^j\}_{j=0}^{\infty}$ is fundamental in $H_p(0,2\pi)$. Let g be a polynomial in x such that $M_p(f - g,1) < \varepsilon(K_p')^{-2}$ and $h = f - g$. Therefore, h belongs to $H_p(0,2\pi)$ and, since g is its own power series, there exists $n_0 > 0$ such that if $m > n_0$, then $f_m = g_m + h_m$, where g_m and h_m denote, respectively, the mth partial sum in power-series expansion of g and h. Hence, for large enough m,

$$M_p(f - f_m,1) = M_p(\{g + h\} - \{g_m + h_m\},1) \leq M_p(h - h_m,1)$$

$$= M_p(h - h_m,1) \leq (K_p')^2 M_p(h,1)$$

$$= (K_p')^2 M_p(f - g,1) < \varepsilon,$$

where the inequality $M_p(h - h_m,1) \leq (K_p')^2 M_p(h,1)$ is due to Theorem 3.12a.

Corollary 3.12.1

If $1 < p < \infty$, $F \in L_p(0,2\pi)$, and $F(t) \cong \Sigma_{n=-\infty}^{\infty} a_n e^{int}$, then

$$\lim_{\substack{m_1 \to \infty \\ m_2 \to \infty}} \left\| F - \sum_{n=-m_2}^{m_1} a_n e^{int} \right\|_p = 0.$$

Proof. Set $f_1(x) = \Sigma_{n=0}^{\infty} a_n x^n$ and $f_2(x) = \Sigma_{n=1}^{\infty} \bar{a}_{-n} x^n$. The result follows from Theorem 3.12b.

Before going to the characterizations of $H_p^*(0,2\pi)$, we shall state several results which, with one exception, are not needed but are of interest in themselves.

Theorem 3.13

If $1 \leq p \leq \infty$ and $F \in L_p(0,2\pi)$, then

$$\lim_{r \to 1} \frac{1}{2\pi} \int_0^{2\pi} \frac{1 - r^2}{1 - 2r\cos(\theta - t) + r^2} F(t)\, dt = F(\theta) \quad \text{a.e.}$$

Proof. Assume $F \geq 0$ and set

$$g(x) = \frac{1}{2\pi} \int_0^{2\pi} \frac{e^{it} + x}{e^{it} - x} F(t)\, dt.$$

By Theorem 3.1, $R_e g(re^{i\theta}) \to F(\theta)$ a.e. and $R_e g(re^{i\theta})$ is the Poisson integral of F.

Theorem 3.14

If f is analytic on $|x| < 1$ such that

$$\sup_r \int_0^{2\pi} |R_e f(re^{i\theta})| \, d\theta < \infty$$

and $0 < p < 1$, then there exists a constant A_p, depending only on p, such that $\sup_r \| I_m f(re^{i\theta}) \|_p \leq A_p \sup_r \| R_e f(re^{i\theta}) \|_p$; consequently f belongs to $H_p(0,2\pi)$.

We shall leave the proof to the reader, inasmuch as it is similar to the proof of Theorem 3.11. The proofs of the following three theorems will also be left to the reader.

Theorem 3.15

If $u(r,\theta)$ is a harmonic function on $|re^{i\theta}| < 1$, $1 \leq p \leq \infty$, and $r_1 < r_2$, then $M_p(u,r_1) \leq M_p(u,r_2)$, where

$$M_p(u,r) = \left\{ \frac{1}{2\pi} \int_0^{2\pi} |u(r,\theta)|^p \, d\theta \right\}^{1/p}$$

for $0 < r < 1$.

Theorem 3.15a

If f is analytic on $|x| < 1$ and $\sup_r M_2(R_e f(re^{i\theta}), r) < \infty$, then $M_2(I_m f, 1) < \infty$; moreover, if $I_m f(0) = 0$, then $M_2(R_e f, r) = M_2(I_m f, r)$.

Theorem 3.15b

If f is analytic on $|x| < 1$, $1 < p < \infty$, and $\sup_r M_p(R_e f(re^{i\theta}), r) < \infty$, then $f \in H_p(0,2\pi)$.

We shall now characterize $H_p^*(0,2\pi)$, $1 < p < \infty$. At the present time there is no satisfactory characterization of $H_\infty^*(0,2\pi)$, and the same can be said about $H_1^*(0,\infty)$. The next theorem is an immediate consequence of Theorem 3.12b.

Theorem 3.16

If $1 < p < \infty$, $T \in H_p^*(0,2\pi)$, $c_m = T(x^m)$, $m = 0,1,2,\ldots$, $g(x) = \Sigma_{n=0}^\infty a_n x^n$, and $g \in H_p(0,2\pi)$, then $T(g) = \Sigma_{m=0}^\infty a_m c_m$.

With regard to the preceding theorem and the function $h(x) = \Sigma_{m=0}^\infty c_m x^m$, we shall show that $h \in H_q(0,2\pi)$.

Theorem 3.17

If $1 < p < \infty$, $p^{-1} + q^{-1} = 1$, and $F \in L_q(0,2\pi)$, then there exists uniquely $h \in H_q(0,2\pi)$ such that

$$\frac{1}{2\pi} \int_0^{2\pi} F(e^{-it})g(e^{it})\,dt = \frac{1}{2\pi} \int_0^{2\pi} g(e^{it})h(e^{-it})\,dt$$

for every $g \in H_p(0,2\pi)$.

Proof. Let $F(e^{it}) \cong \Sigma_{m=-\infty}^{\infty} a_m e^{imt}$ and h be the analytic part of F. By Theorem 3.11 $h \in H_q(0,2\pi)$. Suppose $g \in H_p(0,2\pi)$ and $\varepsilon > 0$. By Theorem 3.10, there exists $r_0 < 1$ such that if $r_0 < r < 1$, then

$$\left\{ \frac{1}{2\pi} \int_0^{2\pi} |g(e^{i\theta}) - g(re^{i\theta})|^p \, d\theta \right\}^{1/p} < \varepsilon(\|F\|_q)^{-1}.$$

By Holder's inequality,

$$\left| \frac{1}{2\pi} \int_0^{2\pi} F(e^{-it})\{g(e^{it}) - g(re^{-it})\}\,dt \right| < \varepsilon.$$

A simple computation gives

$$\frac{1}{2\pi} \int_0^{2\pi} F(e^{-it})g(re^{it})\,dt = \frac{1}{2\pi} \int_0^{2\pi} h(e^{-it})g(re^{it})\,dt.$$

Letting $r \to 1$ gives the desired result. The uniqueness of h follows readily from the fact that $x^n \in H_p(0,2\pi)$, $n = 0,1,\ldots$.

Theorem 3.18

If $1 < p < \infty$, then $H_p^*(0,2\pi)$ is topologically and algebraically isomorphic to $H_q(0,2\pi)$, where $p^{-1} + q^{-1} = 1$; i.e., if $T \in H_p^*(0,2\pi)$, then there exists uniquely an element $h \in H_q(0,2\pi)$ such that

$$T(g) = \frac{1}{2\pi} \int_0^{2\pi} g(e^{it})h(e^{-it})\,dt \tag{3.18a}$$

for every $g \in H_p(0,2\pi)$ and, moreover,

$$\|T\| \le M_q(h,1) \le A_p\|T\|, \tag{3.18b}$$

where A_p is a constant depending only on p. Conversely, every $h \in H_q(0,2\pi)$ uniquely determines an element of $H_p^*(0,2\pi)$ such that (3.18a) and (3.18b) are satisfied.

Proof. Suppose $T \in H_p^*(0,2\pi)$. Since $H_p(0,2\pi)$ is a subspace of $L_p(0,2\pi)$ and $M_p(g,1) = \|g\|_p$ for every $g \in H_p(0,2\pi)$, we can by the Hahn–Banach theorem make a norm extension T' of T to $L_p(0,2\pi)$, Since $L_p^*(0,2\pi) = L_q(0,2\pi)$ (cf. Remark 1.2), there exists uniquely $F \in L_q(0,2\pi)$ such that $\|T\| = \|T'\| = \|F\|_q$ and

$$T(g) = \frac{1}{2\pi} \int_0^{2\pi} g(e^{it})F(e^{-it})\,dt \qquad (3.18c)$$

for every $g \in H_p(0,2\pi)$. Equation (3.18a) now follows from (3.18c) and Theorem 3.17, where, again, h is the analytic part of F. By Theorem 3.11, $M_q(h,1) \le K_q'\|F\|_q = K_q'\|T\|$ and $K_p' = K_q'$, which gives the right side of (3.18b). Inasmuch as

$$\|T\| = \sup_{M_p(g,1)=1} |T(g)| = \sup_{M(g,1)=1} \left| \frac{1}{2\pi} \int_0^{2\pi} g(e^{it})F(e^{-it})\,dt \right|$$

$$= \sup_{M_p(g,1)=1} \left| \frac{1}{2\pi} \int_0^{2\pi} g(e^{it})h(e^{-it})\,dt \right| \le \sup_{\|f\|_p=1} \left\{ \frac{1}{2\pi} \int_0^{2\pi} f(t)h(e^{-it})\,dt \right\}$$

$$= \|h\|_q = M_q(h,1),$$

we have $\|T\| \le M_q(h,1)$.

We shall now characterize $H_1^*(0,2\pi)$. Characterizations exist that are more pleasing than the ones given below; however, we choose the one below to stay within the framework of analytic function theory. The complexities are due to the fact that $H_\infty(0,2\pi) \subsetneqq H_1^*(0,2\pi)$, cf. Example 3.19.1.

Definition 3.3. Γ denotes the class of all pairs (g_1,g_2), where each of g_1 and g_2 is analytic on $|x| < 1$ and

$$\sup_{|x|<1} |R_e g_j(x)| < \infty$$

for $j = 1,2$. We denote this sup by $\|R_e g_j\|_\infty$.

Theorem 3.19

If $T \in H_1^*(0,2\pi)$, then there exists an element $(g_1,g_2) \in \Gamma$ such that

$$T(f) = \frac{1}{2\pi} \int_0^{2\pi} f(e^{i\theta})\{R_e g_1(e^{i\theta}) - iR_e g_2(e^{i\theta})\}\,d\theta; \qquad (3.19a)$$

moreover, $\|T\| \le \{\|R_e g_1\|_\infty^2 + \|R_e g_2\|_\infty^2\}^{1/2}$.

Proof. Suppose $T \in H_1^*(0,2\pi)$. Inasmuch as $H_1(0,2\pi) \subset L_1(0,2\pi)$ we can regard T as being defined on all of $L_1(0,2\pi)$. Consequently, there exists $F \in L_\infty(0,2\pi)$ such that

$$T(h) = \frac{1}{2\pi} \int_0^{2\pi} h(e^{it})\overline{F(t)}\, dt$$

for every $h \in H_1(0,2\pi)$. Set $F = F_1 + iF_2$, where each of F_1 and F_2 is real-valued and belongs to $L_\infty(0,2\pi)$, and

$$g_j(x) = \frac{1}{2\pi} \int_0^{2\pi} \frac{e^{it} + x}{e^{it} - x} F_j(t)\, dt$$

for $j = 1,2$ and $|x| < 1$. Hence

$$R_e g_j(re^{i\theta}) = \frac{1}{2\pi} \int_0^{2\pi} \frac{1 - r^2}{1 - 2r\cos(\theta - t) + r^2} F_j(t)\, dt,$$

$\|R_e g_j\|_\infty \le \|F_j\|_\infty$, and, by Theorem 3.13, $\lim_{r \to 1} R_e g_j(re^{i\theta}) = F_j(\theta)$ a.e., so that $\|R_e g_j\|_\infty = \|F_j\|_\infty$. For $0 < r < 1$,

$$\frac{1}{2\pi} \int_0^{2\pi} h(re^{it})\overline{F(t)}\, dt = \frac{1}{2\pi} \int_0^{2\pi} \left\{ \frac{1}{2\pi} \int_0^{2\pi} \frac{1 - r^2}{1 - 2r\cos(\theta - t) + r^2} h(e^{i\theta})\, d\theta \right\} \overline{F(t)}\, dt$$

$$= \frac{1}{2\pi} \int_0^{2\pi} \left\{ \frac{1}{2\pi} \int_0^{2\pi} \frac{1 - r^2}{1 - 2r\cos(\theta - t) + r^2} \overline{F(t)}\, dt \right\} h(e^{i\theta})\, d\theta$$

$$= \frac{1}{2\pi} \int_0^{2\pi} \{R_e g_1(re^{i\theta}) - iR_e g_2(re^{i\theta})\} h(e^{i\theta})\, d\theta.$$

As $r \to 1$, the last expression approaches

$$\frac{1}{2\pi} \int_0^{2\pi} h(e^{it}) \{R_e g_1(e^{it}) - iR_e g_2(e^{it})\}\, dt,$$

which, in view of Theorem 3.8, is $T(h)$. Finally,

$$\|T\| = \|F\|_\infty \le \{\|R_e g_1\|_\infty^2 + \|R_e g_2\|_\infty^2\}^{1/2}.$$

The following example shows that the pair (g_1, g_2) of the preceding theorem is not unique.

Example 3.19.1. Suppose $F(t) = 2^{-1}(\pi - t)$, $0 \le t \le 2\pi$. Then

$$F \in L_p(0,2\pi), \ 1 \le p \le \infty,$$

and

$$F(t) \cong \frac{i}{2} \sum_{\substack{n = -\infty \\ n \ne 0}}^{\infty} n^{-1} e^{int}.$$

The analytic part of F is essentially $g(x) = i\Sigma_{n=1} n^{-1}x^n$ and

$$I_m g(re^{i\theta}) = \sum_{n=1}^{\infty} n^{-1}r^n \cos n\theta \to \sum_{n=1}^{\infty} n^{-1} \cos n\theta \cong -\log\left|2 \sin \frac{\theta}{2}\right|,$$

which belongs to $L_p(0,2\pi)$ for $p < \infty$ but does not belong to $L_\infty(0,2\pi)$. Hence, $g \notin H_\infty(0,2\pi)$. Also, this shows that $K_p \to \infty$ as $p \to \infty$ (and, therefore, $K_p \to \infty$ as $p \to 1$), where K_p comes from Theorem 3.11. The function F gives rise to an element $T \in H_1^*(0,2\pi)$, which, in accordance with Theorem 3.19, is given by the pair $(g,0)$ with

$$|R_e g(re^{i\theta})| = \lim_{m \to \infty} \left| \sum_{n=1}^{m} n^{-1}r^n \sin n\theta \right| < \pi + 2^{-1}.$$

We have already mentioned that $H_\infty^*(0,2\pi)$ is still a mystery. The progress made so far in this direction is due to a program initiated by Buck, in which $H_\infty(0,2\pi)$ is studied under a "strict topology" (cf. [9], [82], and [13]).

Definition 3.4. $C_A(0,2\pi)$ denotes the collection of all functions g such that g is analytic on $|x| < 1$ and g is continuous on $|x| \le 1$. For each $g \in C_A(0,2\pi)$ we define $\|g\| = \sup_{|x|=1} |g(x)|$.

It is clear that $C_A(0,2\pi)$ is a Banach space and, in fact, can be regarded as a subspace of $C(0,2\pi)$, the continuous functions on $[0,2\pi]$. Hence $C_A^*(0,2\pi)$ is the Banach space $C^*(0,2\pi)/N_A$, where N_A is a closed subspace of $C^*(0,\pi)$ and $T \in N_A$ if and only if $T(f) = 0$ for $f \in C_A(0,2\pi)$. Using the identification between $C^*(0,2\pi)$ and the normalized function of bounded variations on $[0,2\pi]$ it is easy to identify the space N_A. In fact, if $\varphi \in C^*(0,2\pi)$ and

$$\int_0^{2\pi} f \, d\varphi = 0$$

for every $f \in C_A(0,2\pi)$, then taking $f(x) = x^n$, $n = 0,1,2,\ldots$ and applying Theorem 3.9 gives us that $\varphi \in N_A$ if and only if (1) φ is absolutely continuous, (2) φ' is the boundary value of a function $f \in H_1(0,2\pi)$, and (3) φ has mean value zero, i.e., $\int_0^{2\pi} d\varphi = \varphi(2\pi) = 0$.

Theorem 3.20

$C_A^*(0,2\pi) \cong C^*(0,2\pi)/N_A$, where $\varphi \in N_A$ if and only if φ satisfies (1), (2), and (3) of the preceding paragraph.

Before applying these results to problems in approximation theory, we shall make a few remarks about the H_p spaces that are of interest in comparing the geometry of the H_p spaces with the geometry of the L_p spaces. In the case $p \leq 1$ the differences in the geometry are significant. Let us take the case $p = 1$ and look at $H_1(0,2\pi)$. To this end, we first consider the Banach space $B = C[0,2\pi]/C_A^0[0,2\pi]$, where $C_A^0[0,2\pi]$ consists of all $f \in C_A[0,2\pi]$ such that $f(0) = 0$. If $T \in B^*$ and $F \in B$, then (again using the representation of $C^*[0,2\pi]$)

$$T(F) = \int_0^{2\pi} f \, d\varphi$$

where f is any representative of the class F. Since the zero of B is the class $C_A^0(0,2\pi)$, the above equation yields

$$\int_0^{2\pi} e^{in\theta} \, d\varphi(\theta) = 0, \qquad n = 1,2,\ldots.$$

Consequently, Theorem 3.9 gives us

Theorem 3.20a

$H_1(0,2\pi)$ is isomorphic and isometric to the dual space B^* of B, where $B = C[0,2\pi]/C_A^0[0,2\pi]$.

The import of Theorem 3.20a is that the unit sphere of $H_1(0,2\pi)$ must contain extreme points. This follows from the Krein–Milman theorem (cf. [41]) which asserts that if B is a Banach space and $D \subset B^*$ such that it is convex and compact in the weak star topology of B^*, then D contains extreme points (more is true!). In comparison with $H_1(0,2\pi)$, the unit sphere in $L_1(0,2\pi)$ contains no extreme points. The following simple argument (given to me by E. A. Pedersen) shows this. Suppose $f \in L_1(0,2\pi)$ and

$$\frac{1}{2\pi} \int_0^{2\pi} |f(t)| \, dt = 1;$$

then there exists s such that $0 < s < 1$ and

$$\frac{1}{2\pi} \int_0^{s} |f(t)| \, dt = \tfrac{1}{2};$$

if $f_1(t) = 2[\lambda(0,s;t)]f(t)$ and $f_2(t) = 2[\lambda(s,2\pi;t)]f(t)$, where $\lambda(a,b;t)$ is the characteristic function of $[a,b]$, then $\|f_1\|_1 = \|f_2\|_1 = 1$ and $f = 2^{-1}(f_1 + f_2)$; i.e., the unit sphere in $L_1(0,2\pi)$ is locally flat and contains no extreme points. The latter argument easily extends to an abstract L_1 space of the type $L_1(X,S,\mu)$, where X is a set, S a sigma algebra of subsets of S, and μ a countably additive and continuous positive measure on S such that $\mu(X) = 1$. The deep geometric difference between $H_1(0,2\pi)$ and L_1 spaces tells us that there is no way in which $H_1(0,2\pi)$ can be made into a L_1 space.

For the case $0 < p < 1$, Day [17] has shown that there exists no non-trivial continuous linear function on $L_p(0,2\pi)$, whereas Walters ([94] and [95]) has shown that the set of continuous linear functionals on $H_p(0,2\pi)$ is quite extensive and, in fact, separates points of $H_p(0,2\pi)$. Livingston [45] showed that $H_p(0,2\pi)$, $p < 1$, does not have a locally convex topology, i.e., there is no equivalent norm that can be put on $H_p(0,2\pi)$ making it into a Banach space.

The space $H_\infty(0,2\pi)$ is the dual space of $L_1(0,2\pi)/H_1^0(0,2\pi)$, where $f \in H_1^0(0,2\pi)$ if and only if $f \in H_1(0,2\pi)$ and $f(0) = 0$. Consequently, the unit sphere of $H_\infty(0,2\pi)$ contains extreme points. Characterizations of the extreme points of $H_\infty(0,2\pi)$ (cf. [37], p. 138) and $H_1(0,2\pi)$ [18] involve inner and outer functions. These classes tie together Theorem 3.5 with extremum problems and Buerling's elegant theory [10] of characterizing the invariant subspaces of the shift operator in the separable Hilbert space. For a beautiful treatment of these aspects of the theory the reader is referred to the following excellent monographs of Hoffman [37] (which covers a great deal of what we have said) and Helson [30].

We shall conclude our speculative remarks about the comparison of H_p spaces with L_p spaces by noting the import of Theorem 3.11. Using the nomenclature of that theorem, the transformation T_p, which takes $F \in L_p$ to f the analytic part of F, is a projection operator mapping L_p onto H_p and is called the *natural projection* of L_p onto H_p. A deep result in this direction tells us that if $1 \leq p \leq \infty$ and P_p is a bounded projection of L_p onto H_p, then the natural projection T_p is bounded. Hence, it follows from these remarks and Theorem 3.11 that there is no bounded projection from $L_1(L_\infty)$ onto $H_1(H_\infty)$. For more details see [37], pp. 154–156.

We return to problems in approximation theory and consider what may be called a problem of the Runge type—the problem of approximating analytic functions in the spaces $H_p(0,2\pi)$, $1 \leq p < \infty$, and $C_A(0,2\pi)$ with simple rational functions. More specifically, suppose g is an element of one of these spaces, $\delta(g)$ denotes its norm, and $\{\alpha_j\}_{j=1}^\infty$ is a set of distinct numbers such that $|\alpha_j| > 1$. We want to show that there exists a sequence $\{g_n\}_{n=1}^\infty$ of rational functions such that the poles of g_n are included in

$\{\alpha_j\}_{j=1}^\infty$ and $\delta(g - g_n) \to 0$. If $|\alpha_j| \geq 1 + \varepsilon$, $\varepsilon > 0$, then this will always be possible. The critical situation arises when $\lim \sup |\alpha_j| = 1$.

Theorem 3.21

Suppose $1 \leq p < \infty$ and that $\{\alpha_j\}_{j=1}^\infty$ is a sequence of distinct numbers such that $|\alpha_j| > 1$, $j = 1, 2, \ldots$. Then $\{(\alpha_j - x)^{-1}\}_{j=1}^\infty$ is fundamental in $H_p(0,2\pi)$ if and only if the infinite series

$$\sum_{j=0}^\infty (|\alpha_j| - 1) \tag{3.21a}$$

is divergent.

Proof. Suppose $1 < p < \infty$, (3.21a) is divergent, and $\{(\alpha_j - x)^{-1}\}_{j=1}^\infty$ is not fundamental in $H_p(0,2\pi)$. From Theorem 3.18 there exists $h \in H_q(0,2\pi)$ such that $h \not\equiv 0$ and

$$\frac{1}{2\pi} \int_0^{2\pi} (\bar{\alpha}_j - e^{-it})^{-1} h(e^{it}) \, dt = 0, \qquad j = 1, 2, \ldots.$$

If $x_j = \bar{\alpha}_j^{-1}$, the above equations imply that

$$h(x_j) = \frac{1}{2\pi} \int_0^{2\pi} \frac{1}{1 - x_j e^{-it}} h(e^{it}) \, dt = 0, \qquad j = 1, 2, \ldots.$$

It follows from Theorems 3.11, 3.5, and 1.5 that $h \equiv 0$.

Suppose now that (3.21a) converges, $x_j = \bar{\alpha}_j^{-1}$, and B is the Blaschke product constructed from $\{x_j\}_{j=1}^\infty$. Then $B \not\equiv 0$ and

$$B(x_j) = \frac{1}{2\pi} \int_0^{2\pi} (\bar{\alpha}_j - e^{it})^{-1} B(e^{it}) \, dt = 0, \qquad j = 1, 2, \ldots,$$

which shows $\{(\alpha_j - x)^{-1}\}_{j=1}^\infty$ is not fundamental in H_p, $1 < p < \infty$.

For the case $p = 1$, the necessity is proved in the last paragraph. The sufficiency follows from the first paragraph and, say $H_2(0,2\pi)$, since $H_2(0,2\pi)$ is a dense subset of $H_1(0,2\pi)$.

Theorem 3.22

If $\{\alpha_j\}_{j=1}^\infty$ satisfies the hypothesis of Theorem 3.21, then the divergence of (3.21a) is necessary and sufficient in order that $\{(\alpha_j - x)^{-1}\}_{j=1}^\infty$ be fundamental in $C_A(0,2\pi)$.

Proof. Inasmuch as $C_A(0,2\pi)$ is dense in $H_p(0,2\pi)$, $1 \leq p < \infty$, the condition is necessary. Suppose (3.21a) diverges and $\{(\alpha_j - x)^{-1}\}_{j=1}^\infty$ is not fundamental in $C_A(0,2\pi)$. In accordance with Theorem 3.20, there exists a normalized function of bounded variation φ on $[0,2\pi)$ such that $\varphi \notin N_A$ and

$$\int_0^{2\pi} (1 - x_j e^{it})^{-1} \, d\varphi(t) = 0$$

for $x_j = \alpha_j^{-1}, j = 1,2,\ldots$. The analytic function

$$h(x) = \int_0^{2\pi} (1 - xe^{it})^{-1} \, d\varphi(t)$$

is a linear combination of functions with positive real part such that $h(x_j) = 0$. A similar argument shows that $h \equiv 0$. Hence

$$\int_0^{2\pi} e^{int} \, d\varphi(t) = 0, \qquad n = 0,1,\ldots,$$

and $\varphi \in N_A$, which is a contradiction.

The family $\{(\alpha_j - x)^{-1}\}_{j=1}^{\infty}$ has properties similar to families discussed in Chapter 1 (cf. Theorems 1.12 and 1.13). For example, if n is a positive integer, there exist numbers $\{\alpha_j\}_{j=1}^{\infty}$ such that (3.21a) diverges and $\{(\alpha_j - x)^{-n}\}_{j=1}^{\infty}$ is not fundamental in $C_A(0,2\pi)$ [or $H_p(0,2\pi)$]. The details are left to the reader. The condition that $|\alpha_j| > 1$ allows us to go from rational functions to polynomials in Theorems 3.21 and 3.21a. For other facts see [67] or [21].

We conclude this chapter with a few remarks concerning the H_p spaces, $0 < p < 1$, which we have somewhat neglected. For example, interesting applications of these spaces have been found involving the coefficient problem for univalent functions. One such result asserts that if f conformally maps the unit disc on some region R, then $f \in H_p(0,2\pi)$ for $0 < p < \frac{1}{2}$ (cf. [27], pp. 94–98).

Chapter 4

H_p ALGEBRAS

IN THIS CHAPTER we shall study the H_p spaces in the setting of convolution algebras. Aside from the intrinsic interest we have other reasons for doing this; for example, the study of certain closed subspaces of interest in approximation theory are, in fact, closed ideals. We shall illustrate the latter point with the rotational completeness theorem, which tells us when and only when an analytic function, say f, on $|x| < 1$ can be uniformly approximated on compact subsets of $|x| < 1$ by linear combinations of rotations of a second analytic function g on $|x| < 1$.

As our point of departure for this chapter we shall review some of the elementary properties of Banach algebras. A Banach algebra **B** is a Banach space with a multiplication satisfying

$$\|xy\| \leq \|x\| \cdot \|y\|$$

for each $x \in$ **B** and $y \in$ **B**. **B** is a commutative Banach algebra if $xy = yx$ for all $x, y \in$ **B**. *We shall treat only commutative Banach algebras.* **B** may or may not have an identity e, i.e., $ex = x$ all $x \in$ **B**, and all the algebras treated in this chapter fail to have an identity or an approximate identity. An approximate identity in **B** is a directed system of elements $\{e_\alpha\}$ such that $e_\alpha \in$ **B**, $\|e_\alpha\| \leq 1$, all α, and $\lim_\alpha \|e_\alpha x - x\| = 0$ for all $x \in$ **B**.

An ideal I of **B** is a subalgebra of **B** (I is not necessarily norm-complete) having the additional property that $xy \in I$ for $x \in$ **B** and $y \in I$. I is called proper if $\{0\} \subsetneqq I \subsetneqq$ **B**, and throughout this text, unless otherwise stated, *an ideal will always be proper.* An ideal I of **B** is called

(a) *closed* if I is a Banach space,
(b) *prime* if $xy \in I$, then either $x \in I$ or $y \in I$,
(c) *regular* if there exists $u \in B$ such that $x - xu \in I$ for every $x \in B$, and
(d) *maximal* if I is contained in no other (proper) ideal.

If I is an ideal in **B**, then the closure $\bar{I}$ of I is either **B** or a closed ideal in **B**, and the first situation occurs if and only if I is dense in **B**. If I is an ideal, then the factor space **B**/I is an algebra with multiplication defined by $(x + I)(y + I) = xy + I$ and **B**/I is a Banach algebra if $I = \bar{I}$. We note that an ideal I in **B** is regular if and only if the algebra **B**/I contains an identity.

If **B** contains an identity, then every ideal is regular and is contained in a maximal ideal (Zorn's lemma); in general, even if **B** does not contain an identity, every regular ideal is contained in a maximal regular ideal. **B** is called *semisimple* if the only element of **B** which is contained in every regular maximal ideal of **B** is the zero element. A maximal regular ideal in **B** is necessarily closed.

An algebra A is called simple if A contains no proper ideal. If **B** is a commutative Banach algebra and I is an ideal in **B**, then **B**/I is simple if and only if I is a maximal ideal; if **B**/I is simple then either (a) **B**/I is a field or (b) **B**/I has trivial multiplication; i.e., $\alpha\beta = 0$, $\alpha,\beta \in$ **B**/I.

For an exposition of the details involved with the preceding statements the reader is referred to any of the following excellent books—[35], [58], [46], and [72].

We shall need the following results concerning commutative algebras (cf. [54]). If R is a commutative algebra, then R^2 denotes the ideal (which may not be proper) generated by the set of all pairs xy, $x,y \in R$.

Theorem 4.0a

If R is a commutative algebra, $R^2 \neq 0$, and M a maximal ideal in R, then M is not a prime ideal if and only if $R^2 \subset M$.

Proof. The sufficiency is obvious. To prove the necessity suppose $x \in R - M$, $y \in R - M$, and $xy \in M$. If $J = \{z; z \in R \text{ and } xz \in M\}$, then $M \subsetneqq J$, since $y \in J$, and the maximality of M implies $J = R$. If $K = \{z; z \in R \text{ and } zR \subset M\}$, then $M \subsetneqq K(x \in K \text{ for } xR = xJ)$ and $K = R$, since M is maximal. Hence $R^2 \subset M$.

Corollary 4.0.1

If R is a commutative algebra with an identity, then every maximal ideal of R is prime.

Proof. $R = \{eR\} \subset R^2$.

Corollary 4.0.2

If R is a commutative algebra containing a nonprime maximal ideal, then R^2 is contained in the intersection of all such ideals.

Theorem 4.0b

If R is a commutative Banach algebra such that $R^2 \neq 0$, then R contains a nonprime maximal ideal if and only if $R^2 \subsetneqq R$; moreover, each nonprime maximal ideal is a maximal linear subspace of R which contains R^2.

Proof. Suppose $x \in R - R^2$. A Zorn type of argument shows that there exists a maximal linear subspace S of R such that $R^2 \subset S$ and $x \notin S$. Since $SR \subset R^2 \subset S$, S is an ideal. If S is not maximal, then there exists an ideal S' such that $S \subset S'$ and, moreover, $x \in S'$. If $y \in R - S'$, then the linear space (S, y) generated by S and y contains x. Hence, $x = \alpha y + s$, $\alpha \neq 0$ and $s \in S$, or $y = \alpha^{-1}(x - s) \in S'$. This contradiction shows that S is maximal. It is clear that every such maximal ideal arises in this manner.

Corollary 4.0.3

If R is a commutative algebra without identity and M is a maximal ideal in R, then M is regular if and only if M is prime.

Proof. Since R/M is simple, $(R/M)^2 = 0$ or R/M is a field. In the former case $R^2 \subset M$ and in the latter case R/M has an identity.

We shall call on the preceding results later and now return to the domain of analytic function theory. If each of f and g is analytic on $|x| < 1$,

$$f(x) = \sum_{p=0}^{\infty} a_p x^p,$$

and

$$g(x) = \sum_{p=0}^{\infty} b_p x^p,$$

then the convolution product (Hadamard product) $h = g*f$ is defined by

$$h(x) = g*f(x) = \sum_{p=0}^{\infty} a_p b_p x^p. \tag{4.0a}$$

Clearly $g*f = f*g$. A simple computation shows that if $|x| < r < 1$, then

$$g*f(x) = \frac{1}{2\pi i} \int_{|z| \leq r} f(z) g(xz^{-1}) z^{-1} \, dz. \tag{4.0b}$$

In particular, if $1 \leq p$, $1 \leq q$, $f \in H_p(0, 2\pi)$, and $g \in H_q(0, 2\pi)$, then allowing $|z| \to 1$ and applying Theorem 3.8 to (4.0b) gives

$$g*f(x) = \frac{1}{2\pi} \int_0^{2\pi} f(e^{it}) g(xe^{-it}) \, dt. \tag{4.0c}$$

Theorem 4.1

If $1 \leq p \leq \infty$ and each of f and g belongs to $H_p(0,2\pi)$, then $f*g \in H_p(0,2\pi)$ and $M_p(f*g,1) \leq M_p(f,1)M_p(g,1)$; i.e., $H_p(0,2\pi)$ forms a Banach algebra under convolution multiplication.

Proof. If $p = \infty$, then we have immediately from (4.0c) that

$$M_\infty(f*g) \leq M_\infty(f)M_\infty(g).$$

If $1 \leq p < \infty$ and $h = f*g$, then, for $0 < r < 1$,

$$M_p^p(h,r) = \frac{1}{2\pi} \int_0^{2\pi} \left| \frac{1}{2\pi} \int_0^{2\pi} f(e^{it})g(re^{i(\theta-t)}) \, dt \right|^p \, d\theta$$

$$\leq \frac{1}{2\pi} \int_0^{2\pi} \left\{ \frac{1}{2\pi} \int_0^{2\pi} |f(e^{it})|^p |g(re^{i(\theta-t)})|^p \, d\theta \right\} dt$$

$$= \frac{1}{2\pi} \int_0^{2\pi} |g(re^{i(\theta-t)})|^p \left\{ \frac{1}{2\pi} \int_0^{2\pi} |f(e^{it})|^p \, dt \right\} d\theta$$

$$\leq M_p^p(f,1)M_p^p(g,1),$$

the interchange in the order of integration being valid by virtue of the Fubini theorem. To reach the first inequality in the preceding calculations we apply Holder's inequality to $1 \in L_q(0,2\pi)$ and $|f(e^{it})g(re^{i(\theta-t)})| \in L_p(0,2\pi)$, $g(re^{i(\theta-t)})$ being a continuous function of t.

The $H_p(0,2\pi)$ algebras are examples of commutative Banach algebras that fail to have an approximate identity. In fact, suppose $1 \leq p \leq \infty$ and that $\{f_\alpha\}_\alpha$ is a directed set of elements of $H_p(0,2\pi)$ such that $M_p(f_\alpha,1) \leq 1$ and $\lim_\alpha M_p(f_\alpha * g - g,1) = 0$ for every g in $H_p(0,2\pi)$. If $f_\alpha(x) = \sum_{n=0}^\infty a_{n\alpha}x^n$, then taking $g(x) = x^n$ implies $\lim_\alpha a_{n\alpha} = 1$. This together with $M_p(f_\alpha,1) \leq 1$ implies, by the Vitali convergence procedure, that $(1 - x)^{-1} = \sum_{n=0}^\infty x^n$ is in $H_p(0,2\pi)$, which is absurd.

We shall now consider the problem of identifying the maximal ideals of $H_p(0,2\pi)$. Recall that a maximal ideal is necessarily either regular (consequently, closed) or nonprime. We can characterize the regular maximal ideals easily.

Theorem 4.2

If $1 \leq p \leq \infty$ and M is a maximal regular ideal of $H_p(0,2\pi)$, then there exists a unique nonnegative integer n such that if $f(x)$ belongs to $H_p(0,2\pi)$, then f belongs to M if and only if $f^{(n)}(0) = 0$; conversely, for each nonnegative integer n the set of f such that $f^{(n)}(0) = 0$ is a maximal regular ideal.

Proof. Suppose $1 \le p < \infty$, M is a maximal regular ideal in $H_p(0,2\pi)$, and that for each nonnegative integer m there exists $f \in M$ such that

$$f(x) = \sum_{j=0}^{\infty} a_j x^j$$

and $a_m \ne 0$. This implies that if $f_m(x) = (1/a_m)x^m$, then $f_m * f(x) = x^m$ belongs to M. Hence M contains all the polynomials. Since M is regular, it is closed and, by Corollary 2.1.1 $M = H_p(0,2\pi)$ in the case $1 < p < \infty$. If $p = 1$, $h(x) = \sum_{j=0}^{\infty} \alpha_j x^j$, $h_r(x) = \sum_{j=0}^{\infty} \alpha_j r^j x^j$, then by Theorem 3.9, $M_1(h - h_r, 1) \to 0$ as $r \to 1$ and each $h_r(x)$ can be approximated by a polynomial; hence $M = H_1(0,2\pi)$. Consequently, there exists a nonnegative integer n such that f belongs to M if and only if $f^{(n)}(0) = 0$. We show that n is uniquely determined by M by noting that if M_m is subset of $H_p(0,2\pi)$ such that h belongs to M_m if and only if $h^{(m)}(0) = 0$, then M_m is a maximal ideal.

Consider the case $p = \infty$. Using the same argument as above, we see that if M is a maximal ideal, then in $H_\infty(0,2\pi)$ either M contains all the polynomials or there exists a nonnegative integer n such that f belongs to M if and only if $f^{(n)}(0) = 0$. The assumption that M is a maximal regular ideal means M is both closed and prime. Suppose f belongs to $H_\infty(0,2\pi)$, $f(x) = \sum_{p=0}^{\infty} a_p x^p$, and $f_m(x) = \sum_{p=0}^{m} a_m x^m$. Since f belongs to $H_\infty(0,2\pi)$, it also belongs to $H_2(0,2\pi)$ and $M_2(f - f_m, 1) \to 0$ as $m \to \infty$. Hence,

$$\left| (f*f - f_m * f_m)(x) \right| = \left| ([f + f_m]*[f - f_m])(x) \right|$$

$$= \left| \frac{1}{2\pi} \int_0^{2\pi} \{f(xe^{-it}) + f_m(xe^{-it})\}\{f(e^{it}) - f_m(e^{it})\}\, dt \right|$$

$$\le 2M_2(f,1)M_2(f - f_m, 1) \to 0$$

as $m \to \infty$. Hence, $\lim_m \sup_x |(f*f - f_m * f_m)(x)| = 0$. Since f_m is a polynomial and M is closed, $(f*f)(x)$ belongs to M. Since M is prime, f belongs to M. This contradiction completes the proof of Theorem 4.2.[1]

Theorem 4.3

If $1 \le p \le \infty$, then $H_p(0,2\pi)$ is a semisimple Banach algebra.

Proof. Suppose f belongs to $H_p(0,2\pi)$. If f is contained in every maximal regular ideal, then by the previous theorem, $f^{(n)}(0) = 0$ for $n = 0,1,\ldots$. Hence $f \equiv 0$.

---

[1] We have, in fact, proved that $H_\infty * H_\infty \subset C_A$.

To show that there exist nonregular maximal ideals in the $H_p(0,2\pi)$ algebras, we need some additional lemmas and a definition.

If f and g belong to $L_1(0,2\pi)$ and we regard the interval $[0,2\pi]$ as a group with addition mod 2π (the circle group), then

$$(f*g)(t) = \frac{1}{2\pi} \int_0^{2\pi} f(t-s)g(s)\,ds.$$

In view of the Fubini theorem, this convolution product exists for almost all t and represents a function in $L_1(0,2\pi)$.

Lemma 4.4.1

If $p \geq 1$, $q \geq 1$, f belongs to $L_p(0,2\pi)$, and g belongs to $L_q(0,2\pi)$, then $f*g$ belongs to $L_{pq}(0,2\pi)$.

Proof. We can assume $f \geq 0$ and $g \geq 0$. Hence, each of f^p and g^q belongs to $L_1(0,2\pi)$ and

$$\frac{1}{2\pi} \int_0^{2\pi} f(t-s)g(s)\,ds = \|g\|_1 \frac{1}{2\pi} \int_0^{2\pi} f(t-s)[g(s)(\|g\|_1)^{-1}]\,ds$$

$$\leq \|g\|_1 \left\{ \frac{1}{2\pi} \int_0^{2\pi} [f(t-s)]^p [g(s)(\|g\|_1)^{-1}]\,ds \right\}^{1/p}$$

$$= (\|g\|_1)^{1-1/p} \left\{ \frac{1}{2\pi} \int_0^{2\pi} [f(t-s)]^p g(s)\,ds \right\}^{1/p}. \quad (4.4.1a)$$

The inequality results from applying Holder's inequality to

$$\int_0^{2\pi} 1 \cdot f(t-s)\,d\mu(s)$$

where $d\mu(s) = (1/2\pi)[g(s)(\|g\|_1)^{-1}]\,ds$ and noting that f^p and g belong to $L_1(0,2\pi)$, so that f^p*g exists. Also, we have

$$\frac{1}{2\pi} \int_0^{2\pi} f^p(t-s)g(s)\,ds = \|f^p\|_1 \frac{1}{2\pi} \int_0^{2\pi} [f(t-s)]^p \|f^p\|_1^{-1} g(s)\,ds$$

$$\leq \|f^p\|_1 \left\{ \frac{1}{2\pi} \int_0^{2\pi} [f(t-s)]^p (\|f\|_1)^{-p} [g(s)]^q\,ds \right\}^{1/q}$$

$$= \|f^p\|_1^{1-1/q} \left\{ \frac{1}{2\pi} \int_0^{2\pi} [f(t-s)]^p [g(s)]^q\,ds \right\}^{1/q}. \quad (4.4.1b)$$

Upon substituting (4.4.1b) in (4.4.1a), we have

$$\frac{1}{2\pi} \int_0^{2\pi} f(t-s)g(s)\,ds$$
$$\leq \|g\|_1^{(1-1/p)}\|f\|_p^{(1-1/q)}\left\{\frac{1}{2\pi}\int_0^{2\pi}[f(t-s)]^p[g(s)]^q\,ds\right\}^{1/pq}.$$

Therefore,

$$[(f*g)(t)]^{pq} \leq \|g\|_1^{pq(1-1/p)}\|f\|_p^{pq(1-1/q)}\frac{1}{2\pi}\int_0^{2\pi}[f(t-s)]^p[g(s)]^q\,ds,$$

and, upon using Fubini's theorem,

$$\left\{\frac{1}{2\pi}\int_0^{2\pi}[(f*g)(t)]^{pq}\,dt\right\}^{1/pq}$$
$$\leq \|g\|_1^{(1-1/p)}\|f\|_p^{(1-1/q)}[\|f^p\|_1 \cdot \|g^q\|_1]^{1/pq}.$$

Since $\|g\|_1 \leq \|g\|_q$, $\|f^p\|_1 = \|f\|_p^p$, and $\|g^q\|_1 = \|g\|_q^q$,

we have

$$\|f*g\|_{pq} \leq \|f\|_p\|g\|_q.$$

The next lemma is a special case of a gap theorem due to Paley [61]. Paley proved the theorem for $\lambda > 1$; however, for our needs $\lambda > 2$ will be sufficient.

Lemma 4.4.2

If $f(x) = \Sigma_{p=0}^\infty a_p x^p$, $f \in H_1(0,2\pi)$, $\lambda > 2$, and $\{n_j\}_{j=1}^\infty$ is an increasing sequence of integers such that $(n_{j+1})(n_j)^{-1} > \lambda$, $j = 1,2,\ldots$, then $\Sigma_j |a_{n_j}|^2 < \infty$.

Proof. From Theorem 3.5, $f = Bh = Bh^{1/2}h^{1/2}$, so that $f = gk$, where each of g and k belong to $H_2(0,2\pi)$. If $k(x) = \Sigma_{p=0}^\infty b_p x^p$ and $g(x) = \Sigma_{p=0}^\infty d_p x^p$, then

$$|a_{n_j}| = \left| \sum_{i=0}^{n_j} b_i d_{n_j-i} \right|$$
$$\leq \sum_{i=0}^{n_j-1} |b_i| |d_{n_j-i}| + \sum_{i=n_j-1}^{n_j} |b_i| |d_{n_j-i}|.$$

Upon applying Schwarz's inequality to the latter sums, we get

$$|a_{n_j}| \leq M_2(k,1)\left\{\sum_{u=n_j-n_{j-1}}^{n_j} |d_u|^2\right\}^{1/2} + M_2(g,1)\left\{\sum_{u=n_j+1}^{n_j} |b_u|^2\right\}^{1/2},$$

or

$$|a_{n_j}|^2 \leq 2[M_2(k,1)]^2\left\{\sum_{n_j-n_{j-1}}^{n_j} |d_u|^2\right\}^{1/2} + 2[M_2(g,1)]^2\left\{\sum_{n_j-1+1}^{n_j} |b_u|^2\right\}^{1/2}.$$

The gap hypothesis implies $n_{j-1} \leq (\lambda - 1)n_{j-1} \leq n_j - n_{j-1} \leq n_j$, for each j; hence there is no integer u satisfying $n_j - n_{j-1} \leq u \leq n_j$ for more than one j. Consequently, upon summing the above inequality over j we obtain

$$\sum_j |a_{n_j}|^2 \leq 4\{M_2(k,1)M_2(g,1)\}^2.$$

Theorem 4.4

If $1 \leq p \leq \infty$, then $H_p(0,2\pi)$ contains nonprime maximal ideals.

Proof. In accordance with Theorem 4.0b we need only show that $(H_p(0,2\pi))^2 \subsetneq H_p(0,2\pi)$. First suppose $1 < p < \infty$. By Lemma 4.4.1, $(H_p(0,2\pi))^2 \subset H_{p^2}(0,2\pi) \subset H_p(0,2\pi)$. The latter containment is proper, for there exists $F \in L_p(0,2\pi) - L_{p^2}(0,2\pi)$ such that $F \geq 0$. By Theorem 3.11 the analytic part of F, say f, belongs to $H_p(0,2\pi)$. $R_e f(re^{i\theta})$ is given by the Poisson integral of F and by Theorem 3.13, $R_e f(re^{i\theta}) \to F(\theta)$ a.e. It follows readily that f cannot belong to $H_{p^2}(0,2\pi)$.

For the case $p = 1$ we give a proof due to Rudin. In this situation suppose $n_{j+1} > 2n_j$, $j = 1,2,\ldots$, and $f(x) = \sum_{j=1}^\infty j^{-1}x^{n_j}$, so that $f \in H_2(0,2\pi) \subset H_1(0,2\pi)$. If, say, there exist functions k_t and g_t, $t = 1,2,\ldots,m$ such that

$$k_t(x) = \sum_{p=0}^\infty a_{p_t}x^p, g_t(x) = \sum_{p=0}^\infty b_{p_t}x^p, k_t \in H_1(0,2\pi), g_t \in H_1(0,2\pi),$$

and $f = \sum_{t=1}^m k_t {}^* g_t$, then

$$\sum_{j=1}^N j^{-1} \leq \sum_{j=1}^N \sum_{t=1}^m |a_{j_t}b_{j_t}| \leq \sum_{t=1}^m \left\{ \sum_{j=1}^N |b_{j_t}|^2 \sum_{j=1}^N |a_{j_t}|^2 \right\}^{1/2}.$$

By Lemma 4.4.2, the right side of the above inequality is bounded, which is absurd.

Suppose $p = \infty$ and $H_\infty(0,2\pi) \subset (H_\infty(0,2\pi))^2$. Let $f_0(x) = \sum_{j=0}^\infty j^{-2}x^j$, $0^{-2} = 0$, so that $f_0 \in H_\infty(0,2\pi)$. Under the hypothesis $H_\infty(0,2\pi) \subset (H_\infty(0,2\pi))^2$ we can assume $f = f_1^* f_2^* f_3^* f_4$. Hence, if $f_1(x) = \sum_{p=0}^\infty a_{p_j}x^p$, then $j^{-1} = |a_{j1}a_{j2}a_{j3}a_{j4}|^{1/2}$ and, by Schwarz's inequality,

$$\sum_{j=1}^N j^{-1} \leq \left\{ \sum_{j=1}^N |a_{j1}|^2 \sum_{j=1}^N |a_{j2}|^2 \sum_{j=1}^N |a_{j3}|^2 \sum_{j=1}^N |a_{j4}|^2 \right\}^{1/4}.$$

The term on the right is bounded by $\{\Pi_{i=1}^4 M_2(f_i,1)\}^{1/2}$.

Our proof, in the case $p = \infty$, shows that $(C_A(0,2\pi))^2 \subsetneq C_A(0,2\pi)$.

Corollary 4.4.1

Under convolution multiplication $C_A(0,2\pi)$ is a Banach algebra containing both regular and nonregular maximal ideals. A maximal ideal is regular if and only if there exists uniquely a nonnegative integer n such that $M = \{f; f \in C_A(0,2\pi)$ and $f^{(n)}(0) = 0\}$.

In the algebras $H_p(0,2\pi)$ and $C_A(0,2\pi)$ the regular maximal ideals were equivalent to the closed maximal ideals. In general this is not true, as can be seen from the following example. Suppose A is the Banach algebra of all functions f such that f is analytic on $|x| < 1$, continuous on $|x| \leq 1$, and $f(0) = 0$, multiplication in A being the same as pointwise multiplication of functions (not convolution multiplication). Let $M \subset A$ such that $f \in M$ if and only if $f'(0) = 0$. M is the unique nonprimed maximal ideal in A and is closed.

Theorem 4.5

If $1 \leq p < \infty$ and I is a closed ideal in $H_p(0,\infty)$, then there exists a non-negative integer n such that $I \subset M_n$, where $M_n = \{f; f \in H_p(0,2\pi)$ and $f^{(n)}(0) = 0\}$.

Proof. If I is not contained in some M_n, then, as in the proof of Theorem 4.2, I contains all the polynomials. Since I is closed, $I = H_p(0,2\pi)$.

Corollary 4.5.1

If $1 \leq p < \infty$ and I is an ideal in $H_p(0,2\pi)$, then $\bar{I}$ (the closure of I) is an ideal $H_p(0,2\pi)$ if and only if $I \subset M_n$ for some n.

The last theorem and corollary are valid for $C_A(0,2\pi)$ but not for $H_\infty(0,2\pi)$ the difficulty is due to the fact that I need not be prime.

Theorem 4.6

The closed nonregular maximal ideals of $H_\infty(0,2\pi)$ are precisely the closed maximal linear subspaces of $H_\infty(0,2\pi)$ containing $C_A(0,2\pi)$; moreover, if $f \in H_\infty(0,2\pi) - C_A(0,2\pi)$, then there exists a closed maximal nonregular ideal containing f.

Proof. Suppose M is a nonregular maximal ideal in $H_\infty(0,2\pi)$. Then M contains all the polynomials which, in turn, are dense in $C_A(0,2\pi)$; i.e., $C_A(0,2\pi) \subset \bar{M} = M$. Suppose $f \in H_\infty(0,2\pi) - M$. Since M is a closed subspace of $H_\infty(0,2\pi)$, there exists (the Hahn-Banach theorem) a $T \in H_\infty^*(0,2\pi)$ such that $T(f) \neq 0$ and $T(h) = 0$ for $h \in M$. Since $(H_\infty(0,2\pi))^2 \subset C_A(0,2\pi)$, $T^{-1}(0)$ is a nonregular maximal ideal containing M and thus equals M.

Theorem 4.7

If $1 \leq p \leq \infty$ and I is a closed and prime ideal in $H_p(0,2\pi)$, then there exists uniquely a nonnegative integer n such that $I = M_n$.

Theorem 4.8

If $1 \leq p < \infty$ and I is closed ideal in $H_p(0,2\pi)$, then I is the closure of the set S, where $S = \{x^n ; x^n \in I, n = 0,1,2,\ldots\}$; i.e., I is determined by the polynomials it contains.

The proofs of Theorems 4.7 and 4.8 are left to the reader.

Definition 4.1. If $1 \leq p < \infty$ and I is a subset of $H_p(0,\infty)$, then I is called *translation-invariant* if and only if $f_\lambda \in I$ whenever $f \in I$ and $|\lambda| = 1$ [recall $f_\lambda(x) = f(\lambda x)$].

Theorem 4.9

If I is a closed subspace of $H_p(0,2\pi)$, $1 \leq p < \infty$, then I is an ideal of $H_p(0,2\pi)$ if and only if I is translation-invariant.

Proof. If I is an ideal, then by Theorem 4.8, I is translation-invariant. If I is a closed subspace and translation-invariant, then, for $f \in I$ and $h \in H_p(0,2\pi)$,

$$f*h(x) = \frac{1}{2\pi} \int_0^{2\pi} f(xe^{-it})h(e^{it})dt.$$

The integral can be approximated by sums of the type

$$\sigma_n(x) = \frac{1}{2\pi} \sum_{p=0}^{n} f(xe^{-it_p})h(e^{it_p})(t_{p+1} - t_p),$$

so that $M_p(f*h - \sigma_n, 1) \to 0$ as $n \to \infty$, since $f_\lambda \in I$, $\lambda = e^{-it_p}$ and $\sigma_n \in I$.

Theorems 4.8 and 4.9 are usually associated with the spectral-synthesis problem. Suppose f belongs to anyone of the spaces we are discussing and $S(f)$ denotes the closed linear subspace generated by the translates of f. The spectral-synthesis problem is said to be solvable, mod f, if $S(f)$ is generated by the elementary positive-definite functions that it contains. In the situation we are considering, the elementary positive-definite functions are of the form x^n, $n = 0,1,\ldots$. Theorems 4.8 and 4.9 are valid for $C_A(0,2\pi)$ but not for $H_\infty(0,2\pi)$. All the results so far obtained in this chapter can be extended to the space $L_p(G)$, $1 < p \leq \infty$, and $C(G)$, where G is a compact abelian group; and $H_p(G)$, $1 \leq p \leq \infty$, and $C_A(G)$, where G is a compact and connected abelian group. For the definition of these spaces see [50], and for the afore-mentioned extensions see [31] and [78]. The case $L_1(G)$ is completely settled; in fact, $(L_1(G))^2 = L_1(G)$ and, therefore, $L_1(G)$ has no nonprime maximal ideal and even more is true in this particular situation. (cf. [32] and [79]). If G is locally compact, abelian, and not compact, then $L_p(G)$, $1 < p$, is not a convolution algebra. In the case where G is locally compact, not compact, not abelian, unimodular, with a compact center and $1 < p \leq 2$, it is not known if $L_p(G)$ is a convolution algebra.

Theorem 4.10

Suppose $1 \leq p < \infty$, $f \in H_p(0,2\pi)$, and I is the closed ideal generated by f in $H_p(0,2\pi)$. If $h \in H_p(0,2\pi)$, then $h \in I$ if and only if $h^{(m)}(0) = 0$ whenever $f^{(m)}(0) = 0$, $m = 0,1,2,\ldots$.

Proof. The necessity follows readily from Theorem 4.9. The sufficiency follows from Theorem 4.8 and the proof of Theorem 4.2.

We now come to the rotational completeness theorem.

Theorem 4.11

Suppose each of f and h is analytic on $|x| < 1$. Then there exists a sequence

$$f_n(x) = \sum_{p=0}^{n} a_{n_p} f(x_{n_p} x), \qquad (4.11a)$$

$|x_{n_p}| = 1$, $p = 0,1,\ldots,n$ and $n = 0,1,\ldots$, such that $\{f_n\}_{n=1}^{\infty}$ converges in compacta to h on $|x| < 1$ (cf. Definition 1.01b) if and only if $h^{(m)}(0) = 0$ whenever $f^{(m)}(0) = 0$, $m = 0,1,\ldots$.

Proof. Clearly if $f^{(m)}(0) = 0$ and h can be approximated by forms of the type (4.11a), then $h^{(m)}(0) = 0$. To prove the converse let us first suppose f and h have radius of convergence greater than 1, so that each of f and h belong to $H_1(0,2\pi)$. If $h^{(m)}(0) = 0$ whenever $f^{(m)}(0) = 0$, then, in view of Theorem 4.10, $h(x) \simeq (f*k)(x)$ for some k in $H_1(0,2\pi)$. Just as in the proof of Theorem 4.9, h can be approximated in the norm of $H_1(0,2\pi)$ by functions of the type

$$f_n(x) = \sum_{j=0}^{n} f(\bar{x}_{jn}x)h(x_{jn})\Delta_{jn},$$

$|x_{jn}| = 1$ and Δ_{jn} a number. Using Cauchy's integral formula gives, for $|z| \leq r < 1$,

$$|f_n(z) - h(z)| \leq \frac{1}{2\pi} \int_0^{2\pi} |e^{it}|^{-1} |f_n(e^{it}) - h(e^{it})| dt$$

$$\leq (1 - r)^{-1} M_1(f_n - h, 1),$$

which goes to zero as $n \to \infty$.

Suppose now f and h are arbitrary analytic functions satisfying the above hypothesis. Let $\{r_n\}_{n=1}^{\infty}$ be a sequence of numbers satisfying $0 < r_1 < r_2 < \cdots < 1$ and $r_n \to 1$ as $n \to \infty$. For each $n > 1$ let G_n denote the disc about the origin having radius $(r_{n-1})^2$. The functions $f(r_n x)$ and $h(r_n x)$ satisfy the conditions of the special case above, so that for $|z| < r_n$ there exists numbers a_{jn} and x_{jn}, $|x_{jn}| = 1$ such that

$$\left| h(r_n z) - \sum_{j=1}^{m_n} f(r_n x_j z) a_j \right| < \frac{1}{n}.$$

If $x \in G_n$, then there exists z, $|z| < r_n$, such that $x = z r_n$ and

$$\left| h(x) - \sum_{j=1}^{m_n} a_{jn} f(x_{jn} x) \right| = \left| h(r_n z) - \sum_{j=1}^{m_n} a_{jn} f(x_{jn} r_n z) \right| < \frac{1}{n}.$$

This completes the proof of Theorem 4.10.

Whenever f and h satisfy the hypothesis of Theorem 4.11, we say that h can be rotationally approximated by f. Hence, any analytic function on $|x| < 1$ can be rotationally approximated by e^x, or $(1 - x)^{-1}$, etc. The ease with which we obtained the rotational completeness theorem disguises what is basically involved. For a view of this involvement, the reader is referred to the papers of Ditkin, Shilov, and Wiener referred to in [58]. In the next chapter we shall show how the rotational completeness theorem can be applied to obtain algebraic properties of rings of analytic functions.

Chapter 5

THE RING OF
ANALYTIC FUNCTIONS

IN THIS CHAPTER we shall investigate the formal algebraic structure of the
ring R of all functions which are analytic on the disc $|x| < 1$. Multiplication
in R is the Hadamard product; i.e., if $f \in R$, $g \in R$, $f(x) = \Sigma_{p=0}^{\infty} a_p x^p$, and
$g(x) = \Sigma_{p=0}^{\infty} b_p x^p$, then

$$f*g(x) = \sum_{p=0}^{\infty} a_p b_p x^p, \qquad (5.0a)$$

or, what is the same,

$$f*g(x) = \frac{1}{2\pi i} \int_{|z|=r<1} f(z)g(xz^{-1})z^{-1}\, dz. \qquad (5.0b)$$

The topology in R is the compact-open topology or, equivalently, the
topology of convergence in compacta on $|x| < 1$; i.e., if $f_0 \in R$, then a
neighborhood basis at the point f_0 consists of all sets of the form

$$U(f_0 K, \varepsilon) = \{f; f \in R \text{ and } |f(x) - f_0(x)| < \varepsilon \quad \text{for } x \in K\},$$

where K is a compact subset of $|x| < 1$ and $\varepsilon > 0$.

With this topology, it follows easily from (5.0b) that multiplication in R,
say $f*h$, is continuous in each of the variables f and h and is continuous
in both variables at the zero element of R. Consequently, R is a commutative
linear topological ring in the sense of Naimark (cf. [25], p. 168). Moreover,
R has an identity e, where $e(x) = (1 - x)^{-1}$. As a linear topological ring R
is an important concrete example of a ring without continuous inverse;
that is, the mapping $\varphi : h \to h^{-1}$, $h*h^{-1} = e$, is not a continuous mapping.
From the analytic point of view this means that the powerful techniques of
spectral analysis cannot be applied to R.

Before studying the structure of the ring R we shall review some facts from the theory of Banach algebras and the Stone-Čech compactification of sets.

Theorem 5.01

If **B** is a simple commutative Banach algebra with identity e such that $\|e\| = 1$, then **B** is isomorphic to the complex numbers.

Proof. Let e denote the identity of **B** and $f \in$ **B**. We shall first prove that for some complex number λ the element $(\lambda e - f)$ does not have an inverse in **B**. Whenever $(\lambda e - f)^{-1}$ exists we denote it by $R(\lambda, f)$ and $R(\lambda, f)$ is called the *resolvent*. When $(\lambda e - f)^{-1}$ and $(\beta e - f)^{-1}$ exist we get, by a simple computation,

$$R(\lambda, f) - R(\beta, f) = -(\lambda - \beta)R(\lambda, f)R(\beta, f). \tag{5.01a}$$

Equation (5.01a) is called the *resolvent equation* and is extremely important in analysis. If $(\lambda e - f)^{-1}$ exists for every λ and $T \in$ **B*** (the dual of **B**), then $T(R(\lambda, f))$ is an entire analytic function of λ and for $|\lambda| > \|f\|$ we have, from

$$R(\lambda, f) = \lambda^{-1} \sum_{p=0}^{\infty} (\lambda^{-1}f)^p \tag{5.01b}$$

and (5.01a), that $T(R(\lambda, f))$ is bounded. Hence by Liouville's theorem and (5.01b),

$$T(R(\lambda, f)) \equiv \lim_{|\beta| \to \infty} T(T(\beta, f)) = 0.$$

Since the latter relation holds for every $T \in$ **B***, we get $R(\lambda, f) \equiv 0$, which is a contradiction. Hence, for some λ_0, $(\lambda_0 e - f)$ is not invertible. If I denotes the ideal generated by $(\lambda_0 e - f)$, then $I \neq 0$ (unless $\lambda_0 e - f = 0$) since $e \in$ **B** and, since **B** is simple (recall that **B** is simple if **B** has no proper ideals), $I =$ **B**, which contradicts the fact that $(\lambda_0 e - f)$ is not invertible. Consequently, $\lambda_0 e - f = 0$, which completes the proof.

We have actually proved the following corollary, which we do not need but is of interest in itself. If $f \in$ **B**, then the spectrum of f, denoted by $S(\lambda, f)$, consists of all complex numbers λ such that $(\lambda e - f)$ is not invertible.

Corollary 5.01a.

If **B** is a commutative Banach algebra with identity e, $\|e\| = 1$, and $f \in$ **B**, then $S(\lambda, f)$ exists and is compact subset of the complex plane.

Proof. The proof of Theorem 5.01 shows that $S(\lambda, f)$ exists. (5.01b) shows that $\lambda \notin S(\lambda, f)$ for $|\lambda| > \|f\|$ and (5.01a) shows that the complement of $S(\lambda, f)$ in the complex plane is an open set.

One of the virtues of Theorem 5.01 is that, in the case of a commutative Banach algebra with an identity, it allows us to associate the maximal ideals of **B** with certain elements of **B***. Under these hypothesis on **B** every ideal I in **B** is regular ($f - ef = 0 \in I$ for every $f \in$ **B**), and, consequently, if M' is a maximal ideal in **B**, then $\mathbf{B}/M'$ (being simple and having an identity) is isomorphic to the complex numbers. Now for $f \in$ **B** let f' denote the image of f in $\mathbf{B}/M'$ and $M(f) = \lambda_0$, where $\lambda_0 e - f = 0$ in accordance with Theorem 5.01. Clearly M is a linear function on **B** satisfying the additional property $M(fh) = M(f)M(h)$. The argument used in the proof of Theorem 5.01 and Corollary 5.01 shows that $|\lambda_0| \leq \|f\|$ or, what is the same, $M \in$ **B***. If $\|e\| = 1$, then $\|M\| = 1$, since $M(e) = 1$.

Conversely, if $M \in$ **B*** and $M(fh) = M(f)M(h)$, then set $M' = M^{-1}(0)$. Clearly M' is an ideal and $e \notin M'$, since $M(e) = 1$ (unless $M \equiv 0$). Since M is a homomorphism of **B** onto the field of complex numbers (which is simple) and M' is the kernel of M, M' is a maximal ideal.

The elements M in **B*** that we just described are called the *multiplicative elements* of **B***. We have proved the following:

Theorem 5.02

If **B** is a commutative Banach algebra with identity e, $\|e\| = 1$, then the maximal ideas of **B** are given by the multiplicative elements of **B*** having norm equal to unity.

At this point we are on the threshold of the very elegant Gelfand–Lorch theory of Banach algebra and refer the reader to any one of the following books—[20], [35], [46], [58], and [73].

We now turn to the Stone–Čech compactification of the nonnegative integers. We denote the set of nonnegative integers by X and the set of bounded functions (sequences) on X by $B(X)$. Under the usual notions of scalar multiplication and pointwise addition and multiplication of functions, $B(X)$ is a commutative Banach algebra with identity. The maximal ideal space of $B(X)$ is the Stone–Čech compactification of X and is denoted by βX. If $\mathcal{M} \subset B(X)^*$ and denotes the set of multiplicative elements having norm 1, then, in accordance with Theorem 5.02, βX can be identified with $\mathcal{M}$. Under the weak star topology of $B(X)^*$, $\mathcal{M}$ is a closed subset of the unit sphere in $B(X)^*$. Inasmuch as this sphere is compact, $\mathcal{M}$ (and equivalently βX) is a compact space.

Suppose now that $n \in X$ and $M^n(f) = f(n)$ for $f \in B(X)$. Then $M^n \in \beta X$. Hence, X, under the mapping $n \to M^n$, is embedded in βX. Consequently, we can regard X as a subset of βX and, in fact, X is dense in βX and $B(X)$ is isomorphic-isometric to $C(\beta X)$, the space of continuous functions on βX. The proofs of the last assertions are left to the reader (cf. [64] and [23]). Also associated with X is the space $C(X)$ of all functions (sequences) on X. $C(X)$ is a linear topological commutative algebra with identity and has βX for its maximal ideal space (cf. [23]).

We shall now analyze the ring R of analytic functions on $|x| < 1$, where multiplication in R is given by (5.0a). Throughout the remainder of this chapter our development follows verbatim the work of Brooks [8].

Definition 5.1. If n is a nonnegative integer, then M^n denotes the set of all $h \in R$ such that $h^{(n)}(0) = 0$.

Theorem 5.1

If M is a maximal ideal in R, then M is closed if and only if there exists a unique nonnegative integer n such that $M = M^n$.

Proof. Let us show that M^n is a closed maximal ideal for each n. By Definition 5.1 if $f(x) = \Sigma_{p=0}^{\infty} a_p x^p$, then f belongs to M^n if and only if $a_n = 0$. Hence, M^n is a linear subspace of R, and if f belongs to M^n, then $(h*f)$ belongs to M^n for every $h \in R$; i.e., M^n is an ideal. Also, if h belongs to R, then h is in the closure of M^n if and only if there exists a sequence $\{f_j\}_{j=1}^{\infty}$ of elements belonging to M^n such that $\{f_j\}_{j=1}^{\infty}$ converges uniformly in compacta to h on subsets of $|x| < 1$. It follows readily from this that M^n is closed. Since M^n contains every function of the type $k_j(x) = x^j, j = 0, 1, \ldots$, $j \neq n$, M^n is a maximal ideal. Clearly, $M^n \neq M^m$ if $n \neq m$.

Conversely, suppose M is a closed maximal ideal of R and $M \not\subset M^n$ for $n = 0, 1, \ldots$. Then if $n \geq 0$, there exists $f(x)$ in M such that $f(x) = \Sigma_{p=0}^{\infty} a_p x^p$ and $a_n \neq 0$; hence, if $h_n(x) = a_n^{-1} x$, then $(h*f)(x) = x^n$ and belongs to M. This means that M contains all the polynomials and, since M is closed and the polynomials are dense in R, we get the contradiction that $M = R$. Hence $M \subset M^n$ for some n and, since M is maximal, $M = M^n$.

It is implicit in our proof of Theorem 5.1 that a maximal ideal in R is either closed or dense in R.

Suppose M_0 denotes the collection of closed maximal ideals in R. For each M in M_0, R/M is a field and, in fact, is the complex number field, say, C. Theorem 5.1 shows that M_0 is homeomorphic to the set X of nonnegative integers. Inasmuch as an analytic function in $|x| < 1$ is completely determined by the values of itself and its successive derivatives at the origin, the elements of the ring R are completely determined by the mappings of $R \to R/M^n$, $n = 0,1,\ldots$. This means that R is isomorphic to a ring of functions, say R', defined on X. The isomorphism of R onto R' is in fact a topological isomorphism, so the continuous linear functionals on R, say R^*, is the same as the continuous linear functionals on R'.

We shall describe the isomorphism between R and R' more precisely. If f belongs to R and $f(x) = \Sigma_{p=0}^{\infty} a_p x^p$, then the Hadamard formula for the radius of convergence of f tells us that

$$\limsup_p |a_p|^{1/p} \leq 1.$$

For this f we define its image f' in R' to be the function on X satisfying $f'(p) = a_p$, $p = 0,1,\ldots$. Hence, if h is a function on X satisfying $\limsup_p |h(p)|^{1/p} \leq 1$, then h is the image of a function belonging to R and h belongs to R'. We give R' the topology of R. Hence, R' is a subring of the ring of continuous functions $C(X)$ on X (all sequences on X) and contains the ring $B(X)$ of bounded continuous functions on X. The essential fact in going from R to R' is that we *exchange convolution multiplication for pointwise multiplication*; i.e., $(h*f) = h'f'$.

We now proceed to identify the dense maximal ideals in R.

Theorem 5.2

If f belongs to R', then f is a unit in R' (i.e., invertible) if and only if (1) $p \in X$ implies $f(p) \neq 0$, and (2) $\lim_p |f(p)|^{1/p}$ exists and equals 1.

Proof. If f^{-1} exists, then $f^{-1}(p) = (f(p))^{-1}$. Hence, $f(p) \neq 0$ and $\limsup_p |f(p)|^{-1/p} \leq 1$, or, what is the same, $\liminf_p |f(p)|^{1/p} \geq 1$. Since f belongs to R', $\limsup_p |f(p)|^{1/p} \leq 1$; hence $\lim_p |f(p)| = 1$. Conversely, if (1) and (2) hold and we define $h(p) = (f(p))^{-1}$, then h belongs to R' and $fh = e$, where $e(p) = 1, p = 0,1,\ldots$.

Definition 5.2. If f belongs to R' and e denotes the identity of R', then

$$(f \vee e)(p) = \begin{cases} f(p) & \text{if } |f(p)| \geq 1, \\ 1 & \text{if } |f(p)| < 1, \end{cases}$$

and

$$(f \wedge e)(p) = \begin{cases} f(p) & \text{if } |f(p)| < 1, \\ 1 & \text{if } |f(p)| \geq 1. \end{cases}$$

Theorem 5.3

If f belongs to R', then (1) $f \vee e$ and $f \wedge e$ belongs to R', (2) $f \vee e$ is invertible in R', and (3) $f = (f \wedge e)(f \vee e)$.

Proof. (1) and (2) follow immediately from Definition 5.2. The proof of (3) follows from considering the cases $|f(p)| < 1$ and $|f(p)| \geq 1$.

Theorem 5.4

If M and N are distinct maximal ideals in R', then there exist f in $M \cap B(X)$ and q in $N \cap B(X)$ such that $f + q = e$.

Proof. If $M \neq N$, then there exist $k \in M - N$, $h \in R'$, and $g \in N$ such that $hk + g = e$. Since M is an ideal in R', $hk \in M$. If we define $f = hk \wedge e$, then $f \in M \cap B(X)$, since f is bounded and $hk \vee e$ is a unit in R'. Let $A = \{p \in X; |f(p)| < 1\}$, E the characteristic function of A on X, and $q = gE$. Note $g \in N$ and $f(p) + q(p) = 1$, or $f + q = e$. We must now show that q is bounded. For $p \in X - A$, $q(p) = 0$, and for $p \in A$, $|h(p)k(p)| < 1$ and $|g(p)| \leq e(p) + |h(p)k(p)| < 2$.

Theorem 5.5

There exists a one-to-one correspondence between the maximal ideals of R' (equivalently R) and the points of the Stone–Čech compactification of the nonnegative integers. Moreover, if M_1^p, M^p, M_2^p are the maximal ideals of $B(X)$, R', and $C(X)$, respectively, which correspond to a point p in βX, then $M_1^p \cap B(X) \subset M^p \cap B(X) \subset M_2^p$. Finally, if $p \in X$, then $M_2^p \cap R' = M^p$ and $M^p \cap B(X) = M_1^p$.

Proof. Let M be a maximal ideal in R'. Then $M \cap B(X)$ is a prime ideal in $B(X)$ and is contained in a unique maximal ideal M_1^p of $B(X)$, where p is a point of βX. We define the function σ from the set $\mathcal{M}$ of all maximal ideals of R' to the set $\mathcal{M}_B$ of maximal ideals of $B(X)$ by letting $\sigma(M)$ equal the unique maximal ideal M_1^p in $\mathcal{M}_B$ which contains $M \cap B(X)$. If M and N are distinct maximal ideals in $\mathcal{M}$, then $M \cap B(X)$ and $N \cap B(X)$ cannot be contained in the same maximal ideal in $\mathcal{M}_B$ because of Theorem 5.4. Consequently, σ is well defined and is one-to-one. If p belongs to βX and M_2^p is the maximal ideal in $C(X)$ which corresponds to p, then $M_2^p \cap R'$ is an ideal and, hence, contained in a maximal ideal M of R'. Thus

$$M_2^p \cap B(X) \subset M \cap B(X) \subset M_1^q$$

for some $q \in \beta X$. However, $M_2^p \cap B(X) \subset M_1^p$ and $M_2^p \cap B(X)$ is a prime ideal in $B(X)$. Therefore, $p = q$ and σ is onto. Composing σ with the function τ on $\mathcal{M}_B$ into βX, where $\tau(M_1^p) = p$, gives a one-to-one map of $\mathcal{M}$ onto βX. This proves the first two parts of the theorem. Finally, if $p \in X$, then $M_2^p = \{f \in C(X); f(p) = 0\}$, $M^p = \{f \in R'; f(p) = 0\}$, and $M_1^p = \{f \in B(X); f(p) = 0\}$, from which it follows that $M_2^p \cap R' = M^p$ and $M^p \cap B(X) = M_1^p$.

We shall identify the dual space R^* of R, i.e., the space of continuous linear functions from R to the complex numbers. Later we shall show that R^* can be characterized in terms of the dense maximal ideals of R.

Lemma 5.6

If $\{\alpha_n\}_{n=0}^{\infty}$ is a sequence of complex numbers satisfying $\limsup_n |\alpha_n|^{1/n} \leq 1$, and if for each sequence $\{a_n\}_{n=0}^{\infty}$ of complex numbers satisfying the same condition, the series $\Sigma_{n=0}^{\infty} \alpha_n a_n$ converges, then $\limsup_n |\alpha_n|^{1/n} < 1$.

Proof. Suppose the lemma is false and $\{n_k\}_{k=1}^{\infty}$ is an increasing sequence of positive integers such that $\lim_k |\alpha_{n_k}|^{1/n_k} = 1$. Let $a_m = 0$ if $m \neq n_k$ and $a_m = \alpha_{n_k}^{-1}$ if $m = n_k$, $k = 1, 2, \ldots$, $m = 0, 1, \ldots$. Then $\limsup_n |a_n|^{1/n} = 1$ and $\Sigma_{n=0}^{\infty} a_n \alpha_n$ fails to converge. Consequently, the lemma is true.

Let us recall that if each of f and h is analytic, f has radius of convergence $r < 1$, and h has radius of convergence $r_2 > 1$, then the Hadamard product $(f*h)$ has radius of convergence r_2; consequently, $(f*h)(1)$ makes sense.

Definition 5.3. R_0 denotes the subset of R such that f belongs to R_0 if and only if f has radius of convergence greater than 1.

Theorem 5.6

R^* is isomorphic to R_0.

Proof. Suppose we define a mapping φ from R_0 to R^* by $\varphi(h) = T_h$, where

$$T_h(f) = (h*f)(1) = \sum_{p=0}^{\infty} \alpha_p a_p,$$

$h(x) = \Sigma_{p=0}^{\infty} \alpha_p x^p$, and $f(x) = \Sigma_{p=0}^{\infty} a_p x^p$. Clearly φ is well defined and is an isomorphism into R^*. To show that φ is onto R^*, suppose $T \in R^*$ and $\alpha_n = T(f_n)$, where $f_n(x) = x^n$, $n = 0, 1, \ldots$, and $h(x) = \Sigma_{p=0}^{\infty} \alpha_p x^p$. We will show that $h(x)$ has radius of convergence greater than 1. If $g(x)$ belongs to R, $g(x) = \Sigma_{p=0}^{\infty} b_p x^p$, and $g_m(x) = \Sigma_{p=0}^{m} b_p x^p$, then $T(g_m) = \Sigma_{p=0}^{m} \alpha_p b_p \to T(g)$ implies $\Sigma_{p=0}^{\infty} \alpha_p b_p$ is convergent. Hence, from Lemma 5.6, $\{\alpha_p\}_{p=0}^{\infty}$ satisfies $\limsup |\alpha_p|^{1/p} < 1$ and, consequently, h has radius of convergence greater than 1.

The space R^* can be characterized in terms of the dense maximal ideals of R. To do this we again consider the isomorph R' of R in $C(X)$. Several lemmas shall be needed.

Lemma 5.7.1

If $p \in \beta X - X$ and $\{p_\alpha; \alpha \in A\}$ is a net in X converging to p, then for each $n \in X$ there exists an α_0 such that $p_\alpha > n$ for $\alpha \geq \alpha_0$.

Proof. Fix $n \in X$. Since $p \neq j, j = 0,1,\ldots,n$ and βX is a Hausdorff space, there exists an open set U containing p and missing $\{0,1,\ldots,n\}$. Now $p_\alpha \to p$ implies that there exists $\alpha_0 \in A$ such that $p_\alpha \in U$ for $\alpha \geq \alpha_0$.

Definition 5.4. If f belongs to R', then $\bar{f}(p) = |f(p)|^{1/p}$ for $p \neq 0$ and $\bar{f}(0) = 0$.

Lemma 5.7.2

If f belongs to R', then $\bar{f}$ belongs to $B(X)$ and $\bar{f}_\beta(p) \leq 1$ for $p \in \beta X - X$, where $\bar{f}_\beta$ is the continuous extension of $\bar{f}$ to βX.

Proof. Obviously, $\bar{f}$ belongs to $B(X)$. If $p \in \beta X - X$, then there exists a net $\{p_\alpha; \alpha \in A\}$ in X such that $\bar{f}_\beta(p) = \lim_\alpha \bar{f}(p_\alpha)$. For $\varepsilon > 0$, there exists a positive integer N_ε such that $\sup_n \{\bar{f}(n); n > N_\varepsilon\} < 1 + 2^{-1}\varepsilon$, and, by Lemma 5.7.1, there exists $\alpha_0 \in A$ such that $p_\alpha > N_\varepsilon$ for $\alpha \geq \alpha_0$; moreover, there exists $\alpha_1 \in A$ such that $|\bar{f}_p(p) - \bar{f}(p_\alpha)| < 2^{-1}\varepsilon$ for $\alpha \geq \alpha_2$. Since A is a directed set, there exists $\alpha_2 \in A$ such that $\alpha_0 \leq \alpha_2$ and $\alpha_1 \leq \alpha_2$. Hence, for $\alpha \geq \alpha_2, \bar{f}_\beta(p) < 1 + \varepsilon$.

Lemma 5.7.3

If each of f and g belongs to R' and p belongs to $\beta X - X$ such that $\bar{f}_\beta(p) < 1$, then $(\overline{fg})_\beta(p) < 1$.

Proof. $(\overline{fg})_\beta(p) = \bar{f}_\beta(p)\bar{g}_\beta(p)$, inasmuch as $(\overline{fg})(n) = \bar{f}(n)\bar{g}(n)$ for $n \in X$. Hence the proof follows readily from Lemma 5.7.2.

Lemma 5.7.4

If in addition to the hypothesis of Lemma 5.7.3, $\bar{g}_\beta(p) < 1$, then $(\overline{f+g})_\beta(p) < 1$.

Proof. If $n \in X$, then $\overline{(f+g)}(n) = |f(n) + g(n)|^{1/n} \leq 2^{1/n}(\bar{f}(n) \vee \bar{g}(n)) = 2^{1/n}(\bar{f} \vee g)(n)$, where $\vee$ denotes the usual maximum of functions.

Definition 5.5. If p belongs to $\beta X - X$, then

$$J^p = \{f \in R'; \bar{f}_\beta(p) < 1\}.$$

Lemma 5.7.5

If p belongs to $\beta X - X$, then J^p is a prime ideal in R.

Proof. From Lemmas 5.7.3 and 5.7.4, J^p is an ideal in R'. Now is $(\overline{fg})_\beta$ belongs to J^p, then $(\overline{fg})_\beta(p) < 1$. But $(\overline{fg})_\beta(p) = \bar{f}_\beta(p)\bar{g}_\beta(p)$, so, from Lemma 5.7.2, at least one of f and g belongs to J^p.

We denote by R'_0 the isomorph of R_0 (cf. Definition 5.3) in R'.

Theorem 5.7

$R'_0 = \cap \{J^p; p \in \beta X - X\}$.

Proof. If f belongs to R'_0, then $\lim \sup_n \bar{f}(n) = \delta < 1$. Hence, there exists a positive integer n_0 such that for $n > n_0$, $\bar{f}(n) < 2^{-1}(\delta + 1) = \eta < 1$. For a fixed p in $\beta X - X$, there exists a neighborhood U of p such that $j \notin U$, $j = 0,1,\ldots,n_0$. Hence $f(n) < \eta$ for $n \in U \cap X$ and $\bar{f}_\beta(p) \leq \eta < 1$. Therefore, $R'_0 \supseteq \cap \{J^p; p \in \beta X - X\}$. To show the containment in the other direction, let us suppose that $f \notin R'_0$ and $f \in J^p$ for $p \in \beta X - X$. Hence there exists an increasing sequence $\{n_k\}_{k=1}^\infty$ of positive integers such that $\lim_k \bar{f}(n_k) = 1$. This implies that if p_0 belongs to the closure of $\{n_1, n_2, \ldots\}$ on βX, then $\bar{f}_\beta(p_0) = 1$. Since every integer n in X is an isolated point of βX, p_0 belongs to $\beta X - X$. Hence $f \notin J^{p_0}$, and this contradiction gives

$$R'_0 \subseteq \cap \{J^p; p \in \beta X - X\}.$$

Lemma 5.8.1

If f is an element $B(X)$, then f is in an ideal I of $B(X)$ if and only if $(f \wedge e)$ is in I.

Proof. Inasmuch as $(f \vee e)$ is bounded away from zero and

$$f = (f \wedge e)(f \vee e)$$

[cf. (3) of Theorem 5.3] and $(f \vee e)$ is invertible in $B(X)$, the proof of Lemma 5.8.1 follows readily.

Lemma 5.8.2

If $f \in R'$, $p \in \beta X - X$, and $f \in J^p$, then $(f \wedge e) \in M_1^p$, where M_1^p again denotes the maximal ideal in $B(X)$ corresponding to $p \in \beta X$.

Proof. Since $(f \wedge e)$ belongs to $B(X)$, $(f \wedge e) \in M_1^p$ if and only if $(f \wedge e)(p) = 0$, or, what is the same, $|(f \wedge e)(p)| < \varepsilon$ for every $\varepsilon > 0$. Suppose

$0 < \varepsilon < 1$ and $f \in J_p$. From Definitions 5.3 and 5.4, $\bar{f}_\beta(p) = \delta < 1$. Let m be an integer such that $(\delta + 1/2)^n < \varepsilon/2$ for $n > m$. Since $\bar{f}_\beta$ is continuous on βX, let U be a neighborhood of p such that $\bar{f}_\beta(q) < (\delta + 1/2)$ for $q \in U$. Let V be a neighborhood of p such that $V \cap [0,1,\ldots,m]$ is empty. Since X is dense in βX, there exists an integer n in $U \cap V$. Hence, $\bar{f}_\beta(n) < (\delta + 1/2)$, or $|f(n)| < (\delta + 1/2)^n < \varepsilon/2$. Hence, $|(f \wedge e)(n)| = |f(n)| < \varepsilon/2$ and

$$|(f \wedge e)(p)| \leq \varepsilon/2 < \varepsilon.$$

Lemma 5.8.3

If $p \in \beta X$, then $J^p \cap B(X) \subseteq M_1^p$; moreover, if $q \in \beta X$ and $J^p \cap B(X) \subseteq M_1^q$, then $q = p$.

Proof. If $I = J^p \cap B(X)$, then it follows readily that I is a prime ideal in BX. From Lemmas 5.8.2 and 5.8.1 we get $I \subset M_1^p$. In case $p \in X$, this conclusion is trivial. The uniqueness $(p = q)$ follows from the fact that a prime ideal in $B(X)$ is contained in a unique maximal ideal of $B(X)$.

Theorem 5.8

$R_0' = \cap \{M^p : p \in \beta X - X\}$.

Proof. Suppose $p \in \beta X - X$, so that J^p is a prime ideal in R'. If $q \in \beta X - X$ such that $J^p \subset M^q$, then $J^p \cap B(X) \subset (M^q \cap B(X)) \cap (M^p \cap B(X)) \cap M_1^q \cap M_1^p$, so that, by Lemma 5.8.3, $p = q$ and $J^p \subset M^p$. From Theorem 5.7 we have, therefore. $R_0' \subset \cap \{M^p : p \in \beta X - X\}$.

Suppose that $f \in \cap \{M^p ; p \in \beta X - X\}, f \notin R_0'$, and $\{n_k\}_{k=1}^\infty$ is an increasing sequence of integers such that (1) $\lim_k |f(n_k)|^{1/n_k} = \lim_k \bar{f}(n_k) = 1$, and (2) $\bar{f}(n_k) > 0, k = 1, 2, \ldots$. We define $f(n) = f^{-1}(n)$ if $n \in [n_1, n_2, \ldots]$ and $g(n) = 1$ if $n \notin [n_1, n_2, \ldots]$. Clearly $\lim \sup_n \bar{g}(n) = 1$ and $g \in R'$. Let $h = fg$, so that $h(n) = 1$ if $n \in [n_1, n_2, \ldots]$ and $h(n) = f(n)$ if $n \notin [n_1, n_2, \ldots]$. Choose $p \in \beta X - X$ such that $p \in \{n_k\}$. Then $f \in M^p$ implies $h \in M^p$ and $(h \wedge e) \in M^p \cap B(X) \subseteq M_1^p$. Hence $(h \wedge e)_\beta(p) = 0$ and there exists a neighborhood U of p such that $n \in U \cap X$ implies $|(h \wedge e)(n)| < \frac{1}{2}$. However, $p \in \{n_k\}$ implies that there exists k such that $n_k \in U \cap X$ and, hence, $|(h \wedge e)(n_k)| = 1 \neq \frac{1}{2}$. Thus the assumption that $R_0' \subsetneq \{M^p ; p \in \beta X - X\}$ leads to a contradiction.

In view of Theorems 5.6 and 5.8, we have

Corollary 5.8.1

R^*, the dual space of R, is the intersection of the dense maximal ideals in R.

Inasmuch as R is a commutative ring with identity, the set of maximal ideals of R, say $\mathscr{M}$, comes equipped with a natural topology; the *hull-kernel* topology. In fact, for $f \in R$, let $E(f) = \{M \in \mathscr{M} : f \in M\}$. The collection $\{E(f); f \in R\}$ is a basis for the closed sets in the hull-kernel topology of $\mathscr{M}$ (cf. [72], p. 111, or [25], pp. 221–223). Comparing this with the topology of βX, we have the following theorem; the proof is left to the reader.

Theorem 5.9

The maximal ideal space of $\mathscr{M}$ of R with the hull-kernel topology is homeomorphic to βX, the Stone-Čech compactification of the nonnegative integers.

We shall now show how the rotational completeness theorem (Theorem 4.10) can be used to obtain algebraic information about the ring R. For notational convenience we shall work with R' and leave the easy translation of the result to R to the reader. Recall that if $f \in R'$, then $\langle f \rangle$ denotes the principal ideal generated by f and is the intersection of all the ideals in R' containing f.

In terms of R', Theorem 4.10 tells us if f and g are elements of R' and n is a nonnegative integer such that $f \in M^n$ implies $g \in M^n$, then $g \in \langle \bar{f} \rangle$, where $\langle \bar{f} \rangle$ denotes the closure of $\langle f \rangle$.

Theorem 5.10

If $f \in R'$ and $Z(f) = \{n \in X : f(n) = 0\}$, then $\langle \bar{f} \rangle = R'$ if $Z(f) = \theta$ and $\langle \bar{f} \rangle = \cap \{M^n : n \in Z(f)\}$ if $Z(f) \neq \theta$. Hence, the closure of every principal ideal is a principal ideal.

Proof. If $Z(f) = \theta$, then, by the rotational completeness theorem, $e \in \langle \bar{f} \rangle$ and $\langle \bar{f} \rangle = R = \langle \bar{e} \rangle$. If $Z(f) \neq \theta$ and k_f is the characteristic function of $Z(f)$ on X, then the function $e - k_f$ is zero when and only when f is zero; hence $e - k_f \in \langle \bar{f} \rangle$. But $\langle e - k_f \rangle = \cap \{M^n : n \in Z(f)\}$ and $f \in M^n$ for $n \in Z(f)$. Therefore, $\langle \bar{f} \rangle = \langle e - k_f \rangle = \cap \{M^n : n \in Z(f)\}$.

Theorem 5.11

If $f \in R'$, then $\langle f \rangle$ is closed if and only if $f + k_f$ is invertible in R'.

Proof. If $\langle f \rangle = \langle \bar{f} \rangle$, then $\langle f \rangle = \langle e - k_f \rangle$ and there exists $g \in R$ such that $fg = e - k_f$ or $e = k_f + fg$ and $f(n)g(n) = 1$ for $n \notin Z(f)$. Define $h(n) = 1$ if $n \in Z(f)$ and $h(n) = g(n)$ for $n \notin Z(f)$. Hence, $h \in R'$ and $h(f + k_f) = e$. Conversely, if $g \in R$ and $g(f + k_f) = e$, then $g(n) = 1$ for

$n \in Z(f)$ and $g(n) = f^{-1}(n)$ for $n \notin Z(f)$. It follows readily that $g(e - k_f)f = e - k_f$. Hence $\langle \bar{f} \rangle = \langle e - k_f \rangle \subset \langle f \rangle$ and $\langle f \rangle = \langle \bar{f} \rangle$.

Theorem 5.12

An ideal I of R' is closed if and only if it is the intersection of closed maximal ideals. In this case I is a principal ideal; hence closed ideals are principal.

Proof. The sufficiency is obvious. For necessity, suppose I is a closed ideal in R' and $X_0 = \{n \in X : I \in M^n\}$. Then $X_0 \neq \emptyset$ and $I \subset \cap\{M^n : n \in X_0\}$. Fix $f \in I$. Hence $X_0 \subset Z(f)$. Moreover, $|f|^2 \in I$ and

$$Z(|f|^2) = Z(f) = X_0 \cup \{n_1, n_2, \ldots\},$$

$n_i < n_{i+1}$, $i = 1, \ldots$. We shall now construct an element of I whose zero set is X_0. The closed principal ideal generated by that element will be $\cap\{M^n ; n \in X_0\}$ and will be contained in I. Assume I is not a maximal ideal. For each $i \notin X_0$ there exists $g_i \in I$ such that $g_i(n_i) \neq 0$. Let $h_i = |g_i|^2$, so that $h_i \in I$ and $h_i(n_i) > 0$. Let $k_i \in R'$ such that $k_i(n) = 1$ for $n = n_i$ and $k_i(n) = 0$ for $n \neq n_i$. Let h_i' be such that $h_i'(n) = (h_i(n_i))^{-1}$ for $n = n_i$ and zero otherwise. $k_i h_i h_i' = k_{n_i} \in I$. Let q be the characteristic function of $\{n_1, n_2, \ldots\}$ on X and for each n let $q_n = qd_n$, where d_n is the characteristic function of $\{0, 1, \ldots n\}$ on X. Then $\{q_n\}_{n=0}^{\infty}$ converges to q in the topology of R' (i.e., the topology inherited from R) and for each n, q_n is a finite linear combination of the functions k_i. Hence $q_n \in I$ for each n and, since I is closed, $q \in I$. Therefore, $|f|^2 + q \in I$. But $Z(|f|^2 + q) = X_0$.

Theorem 5.13

Every prime ideal in R is contained in a unique maximal ideal. Moreover, if P is a closed prime ideal in R, then P is a maximal ideal.

We leave the proof to the reader.

Chapter 6

PROBLEMS IN APPROXIMATION

IN THIS CHAPTER we shall turn our attention to a more general type of approximation problem and shall give a partial solution to the problem. Briefly, the problem is the following. Suppose f and g are continuous functions on $|z| \leq 1$; then under what conditions can f be uniformly approximated on $|z| \leq 1$ by polynomials in g? Obviously the problem is impossible without some condition on f and g; for example, f and g could be supported on disjoint subsets of $|z| \leq 1$.

The first condition we shall impose is that g be of bounded variation on every rectifiable arc C in $|z| \leq 1$. The purpose of this condition is to enable us to exploit the linear nature of a Stieltjes line integral. For example, under this hypothesis on g, if f can be uniformly approximated by polynomials in g, then

$$\int_C [f(z)]^n \, dg(z) = 0 \tag{6.0a}$$

for every simple closed rectifiable arc C in $|z| \leq 1$, $n = 1, 2, \ldots$. Moreover, the collection $A(g)$ of all such functions f will form a Banach algebra under the sup norm and the usual operations of pointwise addition and multiplication and scalar multiplication.

The above remarks suggest that we look at a simpler problem first. Let g be continuous on $|z| \leq 1$ and of bounded variation on every rectifiable arc contained in $|z| \leq 1$ and let $A(g)$ denote the class of all continuous functions on $|z| \leq 1$ such that

$$\int_\Gamma f(z) \, dg(z) = 0 \tag{6.0b}$$

for every simple closed rectifiable arc Γ. Clearly $A(g)$ is a Banach space and contains every continuous function on $|z| \leq 1$ that can be uniformly approximated by polynomials in g. Our problem now becomes: (1) under what conditions is $A(g)$ a Banach algebra, and (2) if $A(g)$ is a Banach algebra, under what conditions is the set of functions $\{g^p\}_{p=0}^{\infty}$ fundamental in $A(g)$? It is worth noting that while (2) implies (1), the converse is not necessarily true. For example, if $g(z) = z^2$, then $A(g) = C_A(0,2\pi)$.

The problem of when $A(g)$ is a Banach algebra is a simpler problem than the one we originally stated and is of interest in itself. This problem was first raised by R. G. Douglas in connection with the study of the Shilov boundary of certain Banach algebras. In this chapter we are interested in the problem from the point of view of approximation theory and shall show that, with mild restrictions on g, $A(g)$ is an algebra of analytic functions on the Riemann surface generated by g.

Our point of departure in this study is two theorems from the theory of conformal mappings, which we shall not prove. Recall that a Jordan curve in the complex plane is a homeomorphic image of the unit circle.

Theorem 6.01

If R is a simply connected region whose boundary contains more than one point and ω_0 is a point of R, then there exists a unique analytic function h such that h maps R one-to-one onto the disc $|z| < 1$, $h(\omega_0) = 0$, and $h'(\omega_0) > 0$. Moreover, if the boundary of R is a Jordan curve, then h can be extended so that it is a one-to-one continuous map from $\bar{R}$ (the closure of $\bar{R}$) onto $|z| \leq 1$ (cf. [12], p. 96).

Theorem 6.02

Suppose R is a simply connected region whose boundary is a Jordan curve, $\omega_0 \in R$, and h is the unique map of $\bar{R}$ onto $|z| \leq 1$ whose existence is guaranteed by Theorem 6.01. Suppose also R_n, $n = 1,2,\ldots$, is a simply connected region whose boundary is a Jordan curve such that $\bar{R}_{n+1} \subset R_n$, $\bar{R} = \cap_n R_n$, and h_n maps $\bar{R}_n$ onto $|z| \leq 1$ in accordance with Theorem 6.01 ($w_0 \in R_n$). Then the sequence $\{h_n\}_{n=1}^{\infty}$ converges to h uniformly on $\bar{R}$.

The preceding theorem goes back to Courant [14]. We have taken it from Walsh [93], p. 32. The following theorem and corollary are due to Runge [80].

Theorem 6.03

If R is a simply connected region whose boundary is a Jordan curve and f is an analytic function on $\bar{R}$, then f can be uniformly approximated on $\bar{R}$ by simple rational functions whose poles are exterior to $\bar{R}$.

Proof. Since f is analytic on $\bar{R}$ it has a power-series expansion about each point of the boundary of R. Hence, it follows from the Heine-Barel covering theorem that there exists a simply connected region R_0 such that (1) $\bar{R} \subset R_0$, (2) the boundary of R_0 is a rectifiable Jordan curve, and (3) f can be extended to an analytic function on $\bar{R}_0$. Hence, for $z \in \bar{R}$,

$$f(z) = \frac{1}{2\pi} \int_\Gamma \frac{f(u)}{u - z}\, du$$

where Γ is the boundary of R_0. The result follows readily now from the covering theorem applied to $\bar{R}$ and the definition of the above integral.

Corollary 6.03a

Let R be a simply connected region whose boundary is a Jordan curve and $C'_A(R)$ be the set of all functions f that are analytic on $\bar{R}$. For each $f \in C'_A(R)$ set $\|f\| = \sup\{|f(z)|;\ z$ on the boundary of $R\}$. Then $C'_A(R)$ is a Banach space and the set $\{f_n\}_{n=0}^\infty$, $f_n(z) = z^n$, $n = 0,1,\ldots$, is fundamental in R.

In the way of indicating a proof for Corollary 6.03a, note that if $u \notin \bar{R}$, then $(u - z)^{-1} \in C'_A(R)$. Hence, in view of Theorem 6.03, we need only show that every function of the form $(u - z)^{-1}$; $u \notin \bar{R}$, can be approximated by polynomials in z, and this amounts to a typical $\varepsilon - \delta$ argument (cf. [16], pp. 275–276). The proof that $C'_A(R)$ is a Banach space is also a standard argument.

If R is simply connected and the boundary of R is a Jordan curve, then $C_A(R)$ will denote the set of all functions f such that f is analytic on R and continuous on $\bar{R}$. $C_A(R)$ is a Banach space under the sup norm on $\bar{R} - R$. The following three theorems are due to Walsh (cf. [93], pp. 36–39).

Theorem 6.04

If R is a simply connected region whose boundary is a Jordan curve, then the set of functions $\{f_n\}_{n=0}^\infty$, $f_n(z) = z^n$, $n = 0,1,\ldots$, is fundamental in $C_A(R)$.

Proof. Fix $z_0 \in R$ and suppose h, R_n, and h_n are constructed in accordance with Theorems 6.01 and 6.02. The function $k_n = h_n^{-1}(h)$ conformally maps R onto R_n. Hence, if $f \in C_A(R)$, then $f(k_n) \in C'_A(R_n)$, and, by virtue of Theorem 6.02, $\{f(k_n)\}_{n=1}^\infty$ converges uniformly to f on $\bar{R}$. The proof can now be completed with the aid of Corollary 6.03a.

Theorem 6.05

Suppose R is simply connected, $0 \in R$, Γ the boundary of R, Γ a Jordan curve, and f a continuous function on Γ. Then f can be uniformly approximated on Γ by a polynomial in z and z^{-1}.

Proof. We have already proved Theorem 6.05 in the case where $R = \{z; |z| < 1\}$ (cf. Corollary 2.1.1). Hence Theorem 6.05 follows from Theorem 6.01 and Corollary 2.1.1.

We shall use Theorems 6.04 and 6.05 later in this chapter [in the study of $A(g)$] and in the next chapter. Although we shall not make specific use of the next theorem, we shall state it because of its own intrinsic value. It is a consequence of the preceding theorem. Recall that a Jordan arc in the plane is something that is homeomorphic to the interval [0,1].

Theorem 6.06

If Γ is a Jordan arc in the plane and $C(\Gamma)$ denotes the space of continuous functions on Γ normed under the sup norm, then the set $\{f_n\}_{n=0}^{\infty}$, $f_n(z) = z^n$, $n = 0,1,\ldots$ is fundamental in $C(\Gamma)$.

We shall now present some applications of Theorems 6.04 and 6.05.

Theorem 6.07

Suppose R satisfies the hypothesis of Theorem 6.04, h the conformal map of $\bar{R}$ onto $|z| \leq 1$ in accordance with Theorem 6.01, and g the inverse function of h. Then $\{g^n\}_{n=0}^{\infty}$ is fundamental in $C_A(0,2\pi)$.

This follows from Theorem 6.04. We leave it to the reader to combine Theorems 3.9, 6.04, and 6.07 to extend Theorem 3.9.

We shall now show how Theorem 6.05 can be used to solve the Dirichlet problem on $|z| \leq 1$. On $|z| \leq 1$, the Dirichlet problem with respect to the sup norm is the following: If φ is real-valued and continuous on $|z| = 1$, then does there exist a function u such that u is harmonic on $|z| < 1$, u is continuous on $|z| \leq 1$, and $u(z) = \varphi(z)$ for $|z| = 1$?

Lemma 6.08.1

Suppose $0 < r < 1$ and P a polynomial such that $P(0) = 0$. Then for $|z| < r$, $|P(z)| \leq 2M|z|(1 - r)^{-1}$, where $M = \sup\{|R_eP(u)|; |u| = 1\}$.

Proof. For $|z| \leq 1$ set $g(z) = P(z)[2M + P(z)]^{-1}$. Fix z and let $A = g(z)$ and $a = R_e g(z)$. Then $-a \leq |a| \leq M$, $0 \leq M + a$, $0 \leq 4M^2 + 4Ma$, and, consequently, $|A|^2 \leq 4M^2 + 4Ma + |A|^2 = (2M + A)(2M + \bar{A})(2M + \bar{A}) = |2M + A|^2$. Hence, for this fixed z, $|g(z)|^2 = |A|^2|2M + A|^{-2} \leq 1$. Since

$g(0) = 0$, it follows from Schwarz's lemma that $|g(z)| \le |z|$. Consequently, $|P(z)| \le |2M + P(z)| \cdot |z| \le 2M|z| + |P(z)| \cdot |z|$ or $|P(z)| \le 2M|z|(1 - r)^{-1}$.

Theorem 6.08

If φ is a continuous real-valued function on $|z| = 1$, then there exists f such that f is analytic on $|z| < 1$, $R_e f$ is continuous on $|z| \le 1$, and $R_e f(z) = \varphi(z)$ on $|z| = 1$.

Proof. In view of Theorem 6.05, φ can be uniformly approximated by polynomials in z and $\bar{z}$. Since, for $n > m$, $z^n z^{-m} = z^{n-m}$, there exist sequences of polynomials $\{P_j\}_{j=1}^{\infty}$ and $\{Q_j\}_{j=1}^{\infty}$ such that $P_j(0) = Q_j(0) = 0$ $\{P_j + \bar{Q}_j\}_{j=1}^{\infty}$ converges uniformly to φ on $|z| \le 1$. Since $R_e(P_j + \bar{Q}_j) = R_e(P_j + Q_j)$, if we set $f = \lim_j (P_j + Q_j)$, then by Lemma 6.08.1, f is analytic on $|z| < 1$, $R_e f$ is continuous on $|z| \le 1$, and $R_e f = \varphi$ on $|z| = 1$.

The preceding lemma and theorem has been taken from a recent manuscript of Leland [43]. This approach to the afore-mentioned Dirichlet problem fits into the framework of topological analysis and actually requires no use of integration theory. In fact, on $|z| = 1$ Theorem 6.05 or Corollary 2.1.1 is equivalent to the Stone–Weierstrass theorem (cf. [83]) applied to the symmetric (star) algebra generated by $f(z) = z$. Schwarz's lemma can be derived independent of integration theory (cf. [96]). Finally, since the conformal mapping theorem can be established without the use of integration, the techniques of topological analysis can be used to solve the general Dirichlet problem whenever the domains involved have Jordan curves for their boundaries.

We shall now turn to the study of $A(g)$ as a problem in approximation theory. Our presentation is taken in a verbatim manner from the work of Crownover [15]. Later we shall need to use Brouwer's theorem on the invariance of domains. This theorem tells us that if A and B are subsets of the complex plane and h is a homeomorphism of A onto B, then interior points A map onto interior points of B and boundary points of A map onto boundary points of B (cf. [38], p. 95).

We shall now present some of Crownover's theory of $A(g)$.

Definition 6.1. Let D be the inside of a circle and g be a function in $C(\bar{D})$ that is of bounded variation on each rectifiable curve C contained in D. We denote by $A(g;D)$ the collection of all functions in $C(\bar{D})$ such that

$$\int_C f \, dg = 0$$

for each rectifiable curve C contained in D. $U = \{z : |z| < 1\}$.

We note that $A(g;D)$ is always a Banach space under sup norm, and contains the linear space spanning the functions $1, g, g^2, \ldots$, just as $A(g)$ has these properties. Also, we have that $A(g)$ is the same as $A(g;U)$. For the special case in which $g(z) = z$, we write $A(z)$ instead of $A(g)$, and $A(z;D)$ instead of $A(g;D)$. The purpose of introducing the notation $A(g;D)$ is to facilitate the study of $A(g)$ locally.

Theorem 6.1

Let D be the inside of a circle. If g is continuous on $\bar{D}$, then a necessary and sufficient condition that g be of bounded variation on each simple closed rectifiable curve in $\bar{D}$ is that g satisfy a uniform Lipschitz condition on $\bar{D}$. That is, that there exist a $K > 0$ such that for arbitrary z and z' in $\bar{D}$, then $|g(z) - g(z')| \leq K|z - z'|$.

Proof. That the condition is sufficient is immediately clear. Suppose the condition is not necessary. Then for each positive integer n there exists points z_n and z'_n in $\bar{D}$ for which

$$|g(z_n) - g(z'_n)| > n|z_n - z'_n|. \tag{6.1a}$$

We note at this time that if $\{n_j\}_{j=1}^{\infty}$ is a subsequence of the sequence of positive integers, and if $\xi_j = z_{n_j}$ and $\xi'_j = z'_{n_j}$, then

$$|g(\xi_j) - g(\xi'_j)| > j|\xi_j - \xi'_j|.$$

That is, inequality (6.1a) is preserved under the taking of subsequences.

Let z_0 be a cluster point of $\{z_n\}_{n=1}^{\infty}$. There exists a subsequence $\{\xi_j\}_{j=1}^{\infty}$ of $\{z_n\}_{n=1}^{\infty}$ that converges to z_0. Let z'_0 be an arbitrary cluster point of $\{\xi'_j\}_{j=0}^{\infty}$. Then $z_0 = z'_0$; for if not, there exist subsequences $\{t_k\}_{k=1}^{\infty}$ and $\{t'_k\}_{k=1}^{\infty}$ of $\{\xi_j\}_{j=0}^{\infty}$ and $\{\xi'_j\}_{j=1}^{\infty}$, respectively, such that $\lim_{k \to \infty} t_k = z_0$, $\lim_{k \to \infty} t'_k = z'_0$, and $|g(t_k) - g(t'_k)| > k|t_k - t'_k|$. It is easy to see that this contradicts the continuity of g.

Thus we can assume without loss of generality that the sequences $\{z_n\}_{n=1}^{\infty}$ and $\{z'_n\}_{n=1}^{\infty}$ each have limit z_0, for some z_0 in $\bar{D}$. We can also assume for each $n = 1,2,3,\ldots$ that

$$|z_n - z_0| < \frac{1}{2n^3} \quad \text{and} \quad |z'_n - z_0| < \frac{1}{2n^3}.$$

We now observe for each $n = 1,2,3,\ldots$ that there exist open sets W_n and W'_n containing z_n and z'_n, respectively, such that if ξ_n is in W_n and ξ'_n is in W'_n, then

$$|g(\xi_n) - g(\xi'_n)| > n|\xi_n - \xi'_n|.$$

This fact follows easily from the continuity of g. It therefore follows that we can assume for each $n = 1,2,3,\ldots$ that the points z_n, and z_0, and z'_n are not on the same straight line.

Again by taking subsequences if necessary, we can assume that the straight-line segment $\overline{z_n z'_n}$ lies inside a circular neighborhood N_n centered at z_0, whose closure $\overline{N_n}$ misses the straight line segment $\overline{z_{n-1} z'_{n-1}}$, for $n = 2,3,\ldots$.

For $n = 1,2,3,\ldots$, let k_n be the positive integer such that $k_n|z_n - z'_n| \leq 1/n^2$ and $(k_n + 1)|z_n - z'_n| > 1/n^2$. Since $|z_n - z'_n| < 1/n^3$, then $n^2|z_n - z'_n| < 1/n$ and

$$1 - n^2|z_n - z'_n| > 1 - \frac{1}{n}.$$

On the other hand, $1 \geq n^2 k_n|z_n - z'_n| > 1 - n^2|z_n - z'_n|$. Therefore,

$$1 \geq n^2 k_n|z_n - z'_n| > 1 - \frac{1}{n}$$

and

$$\lim_{n \to \infty} n^2 k_n|z_n - z'_n| = 1.$$

From this we conclude that

$$\sum_{n=1}^{\infty} k_n|z_n - z'_n| < \infty,$$

but that

$$\sum_{n=1}^{\infty} nk_n|z_n - z'_n| = \infty.$$

Since the straight-line segment $\overline{z_n z'_n}$ lies in the open set $N_n - \overline{N_{n+1}}$, we can find points z_{np}, $p = 1,\ldots,k_n$, on the line through z_n perpendicular to $\overline{z_n z'_n}$, and points $z'_{n,p}$ such that the line segment $\overline{z_{n,p} z'_{n,p}}$, $p = 1,\ldots,k_n$, is parallel to $\overline{z_n z'_n}$, contained in $N_n - \overline{N_{n+1}}$, and such that

$$|g(z_{n,p}) - g(z'_{n,p})| > n|z_{n,p} - z'_{n,p}|.$$

We now let A be the arc obtained by connecting the line segments $\overline{z_{n,p} z'_{n,p}}$. A will be rectifiable, in fact, of length less than

$$\sum_{n=1}^{\infty} k_n|z_n - z'_n| + 2\sum_{n=1}^{\infty} \frac{1}{n^3} + \sum_{n=1}^{\infty} \frac{2\pi}{n^3}.$$

This is seen as follows.

The sum of the lengths of the line segment $\overline{z_{n,p} z'_{n,p}}$ is equal to

$$\sum_{n=1}^{\infty} k_n|z_n - z'_n|.$$

The sum of the lengths of the line segments connecting the k_n line segments $z_{n,p} z'_{n,p}$ for a fixed n is less than

$$\sum_{n=1}^{\infty} \frac{1}{n^3};$$

the sum of the lengths of the connecting line segments that are directed toward the origin is less than

$$\sum_{n=1}^{\infty} \frac{1}{n^3};$$

and, finally, the sum of the connecting arcs that are on the boundaries of the neighborhoods $\{N_n\}_{n=1}^{\infty}$ is less than

$$\sum_{n=1}^{\infty} \frac{2\pi}{n^3}.$$

However, the variation of g over A is unbounded. It is at least as large as the sum of the variations of g over the line segments $\overline{z_{n,p} z'_{n,p}}$, $p = 1, \ldots, k_n$ and $n = 1,2,3,\ldots$, and the variation of g over each of these is at least as large as $|g(z_{n,p}) - g(z'_{n,p})| > n|z_{n,p} - z'_{n,p}|$. Thus the variation of g over A is at least as large as

$$\sum_{k=1}^{\infty} nk_n |z_n - z'_n| = \infty.$$

Since we have found a rectifiable arc A contained in $\bar{D}$ over which the variation of g is unbounded, it follows that there exist simple closed rectifiable curves in $\bar{D}$ for which the variation of g is unbounded. Thus we have a contradiction, and the theorem is proved.

The argument used to prove the following theorem is a standard one in complex-function theory. We leave the details to the reader.

Theorem 6.2
A function f in $C(\bar{D})$ is in $A(g; D)$ if and only if $\int_T f \, dg = 0$ for each triangle T contained in D.

Theorem 6.3
Let Q be the set of points in U, each of which is contained in no circular neighborhood D such that $A(g; D)$ is an algebra. Then Q is a perfect set. In particular, if Q is countable and closed, then Q is the empty set.

Proof. Suppose z_0 is in Q and that z_0 is not a limit point of Q. Then there exists a circular neighborhood D of z_0 that contains no other points of Q. We shall show that $A(g;D)$ is an algebra. For this purpose, it suffices to show that f^2 is in $A(g;D)$ whenever f is in $A(g;D)$. By Theorem 6.2, we need only show that $\int_T f^2 \, dg = 0$ for each triangle T contained in D.

Let T be a triangle contained in D, such that z_0 is not in T or in the inside of T. Let T' be the union of T and the inside of T. Then T' is a compact subset of D. For each z in T', there is a number $r > 0$ such that if $D(z,r)$ is a circular neighborhood of z with radius r, then $A(g;D(z,r))$ is an algebra. Moreover, $A(g;D(z;r/2))$ is also an algebra. Since T' is compact, there exists a finite number of points, $z_1, \ldots, z_n$ and corresponding positive numbers $r_1, \ldots, r_n$ such that $\{D(z_n, r_1/2), \ldots, D(z_n, r_n/2)\}$ covers T'. Let r_0 be the smallest of the numbers $r_1/2, \ldots, r_n/2$. It is clear that for any z in T', the set $D(z, r_0)$ is contained in $D(z_i, r_i)$ for some $i = 1, 2, \ldots, n$, and that $A(g;D(z, r_0))$ is an algebra.

We now join the midpoints of the sides of T, and successively the midpoints of the sides of the resulting triangles, until we have a network of triangles $\{T_j\}_{j=1}^{p}$, each contained in a circular neighborhood of radius less than r_0, and such that

$$\int_T f^2 \, dg = \sum_{j=1}^{p} \int_{T_j} f^2 \, dg.$$

But the right side of this equation is zero, and so $\int_T f^2 \, dg = 0$.

Now consider the case for which T is a triangle and z_0 is in T. We can assume without loss of generality that z_0 is a vertex of T, for otherwise we could split T into two triangles T_1 and T_2 having z_0 as a vertex and then

$$\int_T f^2 \, dg \qquad \int_{T_1} f^2 \, dg + \int_{T_2} f^2 \, dg.$$

Let $\varepsilon > 0$ be given. We split T into a triangle T_0 with z_0 as a vertex and a polygon P. Now

$$\int_P f^2 \, dg = 0,$$

since P can be split into two triangles for which the case already proved applies. Hence

$$\int_T f^2 \, dg = \int_{T_0} f^2 \, dg.$$

But we can choose T_0 small enough so that $|T_0|$, the length of T_0, is less than $\varepsilon/\|f\|^2 K$. Then

$$\left| \int_T f^2 \, dg \right| = \left| \int_{T_0} f^2 \, dg \right| \leq \|f\|^2 V(g;T_0) \leq \|f\|^2 - K|T_0| < \varepsilon.$$

Therefore,

$$\int_T f^2 \, dg = 0.$$

The only case that remains is that for which z_0 is in the inside of T. But we can reduce this to the previous case by splitting T into three triangles connecting the vertices of T and z_0.

Thus we have proved the part of the theorem which says that Q is perfect. Now if Q is countable and closed we get that Q is empty, since it is known that no nonempty, closed, countable, perfect set exists in the plane (cf. [36], p. 88).

The following theorem is an application of the rotational completeness theorem (cf. Theorem 4.10).

Theorem 6.4

Let F be a function that is analytic on U, and such that $F'(0) \neq 0$. Then $A(g;D)$ is an algebra if and only if, for each f in $A(g;D)$ having norm less than 1, $F(f)$ is in $A(g;D)$.

Proof. Certainly if $A(g;D)$ is an algebra, and f is in $A(g,D)$ with norm less than 1, then each such function $F(f)$ is also in $A(g;D)$. On the other hand, suppose f is in $A(g;D)$. We show that f^2 is in $A(g;D)$ and, hence, $A(g;D)$ will then be an algebra. We can assume without loss of generality that $\|f\| < 1$; for if not, then we work with $f/\|f\| + 1$, which has norm less than 1, and f^2 is in $A(g;D)$ if and only if $(f/\|f\| + 1)^2$ is in $A(g;D)$.

Since af has norm less than 1 for $|a| = 1$, the hypothesis of this theorem gives that $F_a(f)$ is in $A(g;D)$ for each a with $|a| = 1$. Let $h(z) = z^2$. Since $h^{(n)}(0) = 0$ except when $n = 2$, the rotational completeness theorem gives us that h can be uniformly approximated on compact subsets of U by finite linear combinations of $\{F_a : |a| = 1\}$. Since $f(\overline{D})$ is a compact subset of U, it follows that f^2 can be uniformly approximated by finite linear combinations of $\{F_a(f) : |a| = 1\}$. But these linear combinations are in $A(g;D)$, and hence f^2 is in $A(g;D)$.

We remark that this theorem tells us, for instance, that $A(g;D)$ will be an algebra if for each f in $A(g;D)$, the function e^f is also in $A(g;D)$.

Definition 6.2. We shall denote by $L(g;D)$ the collection of all functions f in $A(g;D)$ which satisfy a uniform Lipschitz condition on each compact subset of D.

We note that $L(g;D)$ always contains the linear space spanning the functions $1, g, g^2, \dots$. If $D = U$, we shall write $L(g)$ instead of $L(g;D)$.

Theorem 6.5
   If f is in $A(g;D)$ and h is in $L(g;D)$, then fh is in $A(g;D)$.

   Proof. For any triangles T_0 contained in D, there will exist a nested sequence of triangle $\{T_n\}_{n=0}^{\infty}$ such that

$$\left| \int_{T_0} f \, dg \right| \leq \varepsilon K^2 d(T_0) |T_0|,$$

and the theorem follows.

   We remark that we have at the same time shown that $L(g;D)$ is an algebra. In the case of $A(z)$, which consists of the functions that are continuous on $\overline{U}$ and analytic on U, we see that $L(g)$ is actually the same as $A(g)$. In the case where $g(z) = x$, where x is the real part of z, $A(g)$ can be identified with $C([-1,+1])$. In this case $L(g)$ is not all of $A(g)$, for there are certainly continuous functions on $[-1,+1]$ that are far from being Lipschitzian. However, $L(g)$ in this case does contain all polynomials in x, and these are dense in $C[-1,+1]$. Thus $L(g)$ is itself dense in $A(g)$. This might lead one to suspect that $L(g;D)$ is always dense in $A(g;D)$. The following is an example showing that this does not necessarily happen. Let $h(z) = z/\sqrt{|z|}$, for z in $\overline{U}$, and let $g(z) = h^2(z) = z^2/|z|$.

Theorem 6.6
   Suppose D is a circular neighborhood such that $\overline{D}$ is contained in U, and such that g is one-to-one on $\overline{D}$. Let f be any function in $A(g;D)$ and C be any rectifiable curve contained in D. Then for any z_0 in the inside of C, we have

$$f(z) = \frac{\pm 1}{2\pi i} \int_C \frac{f}{g - g(z_0)} \, dg.$$

   Proof. For any z_0 in $\overline{D} - C$, we have

$$\int_C \frac{dg(s)}{f(s) - g(z_0)} = \int_{g(C)} \frac{dw}{w - w_0},$$

where $w = g(s)$ and $w_0 = g(z_0)$. Since g is a homeomorphism on $\overline{D}$, the Brouwer theorem gives us that $g(z_0)$ is in the inside of $g(C)$ if and only if z_0

is in the inside of C. Therefore,

$$\int_C \frac{dg(s)}{g(s) - g(z_0)} = \pm 2\pi i \quad \text{or} \quad 0,$$

depending on whether or not z_0 is in the inside of C.

Let C' denote the union of C and the inside of C. For z_0 in $\bar{D} - C$, we get by the polynomial approximation theorem of Walsh (cf. Theorem 6.04), that there exists a sequence of polynomials in g, $\{P_n(g)\}_{n=1}^\infty$, that converges uniformly to $1/g - g(z_0)$ on C'. By Theorem 6.5, fg'' is in $A(g;D)$ for $n = 1,2,3,\ldots$. Therefore,

$$\int_C f P_n(g) \, dg = 0$$

and hence

$$\frac{1}{2\pi i} \int_C \frac{f \, dg}{g - g(z_0)} = 0.$$

As in the proof of the classical Cauchy integral formula, we can conclude for z_0 in the inside of C that

$$\frac{1}{2\pi i} \int_C \frac{f(s) - f(z_0)}{g(s) - g(z_0)} \, dg(s) = \frac{1}{2\pi i} \int_{C_0} \frac{f(s) - f(z_0)}{g(s) - g(z_0)} \, dg(s),$$

for any circle C_0 centered at z_0 and contained in the inside of C.

Let $\theta(s) = [f(s) - f(z_0)]/[g(s) - g(z_0)]$, and let $\{C_n\}_{n=1}^\infty$ be a nested sequence of circles centered at z_0, contained in the inside of C, and having radii tending to zero. For any positive integers m and n,

$$\frac{1}{2\pi i} \int_{C_n} \theta(s) g^m(s) \, dg(s) = g^m(z_0) \frac{1}{2\pi i} \int_{C_n} \theta(s) \, dg(s).$$

Let C'_n denote the union of C_n and the inside of C_n. Let h_n be a one-to-one mapping from $g(C'_n)$ onto $\bar{U}$ that is analytic on the interior of $g(C'_n)$. We can get such a mapping by first applying the Riemann mapping theorem to the interior of $g(C'_n)$ and U, and extending this mapping in a one-to-one manner to the closures $g(C'_n)$ and $\bar{U}$ (cf. Theorem 6.01). We can, moreover, choose h_n so that $h_n(g(z_0)) = 0$ and $h'_n(g(z_0)) > 0$. Since $h_n(g)$ can be uniformly approximated by polynomials in g on C'_n (cf. [10], p. 430), it follows that

$$\frac{1}{2\pi i} \int_{C_n} \theta(s) h_n^p(g(s)) \, dg(s) = 0, \qquad p = 1,2,3,\ldots.$$

Let $w = g(t)$. The functions θ and $h_n^p(g)$ are continuous on C_n, and h_n is one-to-one on $g(C_n)$. Therefore,

$$\frac{1}{2\pi i} \int_{|w|=1} \theta(g^{-1}(h_n^{-1}(w)))w^p dh_n^{-1}(w) = 0, \qquad p = 1,2,3,\ldots.$$

Now the restriction of h_n^{-1} to the unit circle is of bounded variation since its image, $g(C_n)$, is rectifiable. Since h_n^{-1} is analytic on U, we get that the restriction on h_n^{-1} to the unit circle satisfies the condition

$$\int_0^{2\pi} e^{int} \, dh_n^{-1}(e^{it}) = 0, \qquad n = 1,2,3,\ldots.$$

Therefore, this restriction is absolutely continuous, and hence for $p = 1,2,3,\ldots,$

$$\frac{1}{2\pi} \int_0^{2\pi} \theta(g^{-1}(h_n^{-1}(e^{it})))e^{ipt}(h_n^{-1}(e^{it}))'e^{it} \, dt = 0.$$

Now let $a_n(t) = \theta(g^{-1}(h_n^{-1}(e^{it})))(h_n^{-1}(e^{it}))'e^{it}$. By Theorem 3.9 there is an $H_1(0,2\pi)$ function, A_n, such that

(a) $\displaystyle\lim_{r \to 1} A_n(re^{it}) = a_n(t)$ a.e.

and

(b) $\displaystyle\lim_{r \to 1} \frac{1}{2\pi} \int_0^{2\pi} |A_n(re^{it}) - a_n(t)| \, dt = 0.$

From (b) we get that

$$\lim_{r \to 1} \frac{1}{2\pi} \int_0^{2\pi} [A_n(re^{it}) - a_n(t)] \, dt = 0,$$

or that

$$\lim_{r \to 1} \frac{1}{2\pi} \int_0^{2\pi} A_n(re^{it}) \, dt = \frac{1}{2\pi} \int_0^{2\pi} a_n(t) \, dt$$
$$= \int_{C_n} \theta(s) \, dg(s) = \int_C \theta(s) \, dg(s).$$

Thus

$$A_n(0) = \int_C \theta(s) \, dg(s), \qquad n = 1,2,3,\ldots.$$

On the other hand, (a) says that

$$\lim_{r \to 1} A_n(re^{it}) = [f(g^{-1}(h_n^{-1}(e^{it}))) - f(z_0)]\frac{[h_n^{-1}(e^{it})]'e^{it}}{h_n^{-1}(e^{it}) - g(z_0)} \text{a.e.}$$

For each $p = 1,2,3,\dots,$

$$\frac{1}{2\pi} \int\limits^{2\pi} [f(g^{-1}(h_n^{-1}(e^{it}))) - f(z_0)]e^{ipt}\,dt$$

$$= \frac{1}{2\pi i p} \int\limits_0^{2\pi} f(g^{-1}(h_n^{-1}(e^{it})))\,de^{ipt}$$

$$= \frac{1}{2\pi i p} \int\limits_{|w|=1} f(g^{-1}(h_n^{-1}(w)))\,dw^p$$

$$= \frac{1}{2\pi i p} \int\limits_{C_n} f(s)\,dh_n^p(g(s)) = 0.$$

Since $f(g^{-1}(h_n^{-1}(w))) - f(z_0)$ is continuous, Theorem 3.8 applies and gives us that $f(g^{-1}(h_n^{-1}(e^{it}))) - f(z_0)$ is the almost-everywhere radial limit of an $H_1(0,2\pi)$ function, say F_n. Thus

$$\lim_{r \to 1} A_n(re^{it}) = \lim_{r \to 1} F_n(re^{it})\frac{[h_n^{-1}(e^{it})]'e^{it}}{h_n^{-1}(e^{it}) - g(z_0)} \text{a.e.}$$

We now show that

$$\lim_{r \to 1} \frac{z(d/dz)h_n^{-1}(z)}{h^{-1}(z) - h_n^{-1}(0)} = \frac{[h_n^{-1}(e^{it})]'e^{it}}{h_n^{-1}(e^{it}) - g(z_0)} \text{a.e.,} \tag{6.6a}$$

and that $z(d/dz)h_n^{-1}(z)/[h_n^{-1}(z) - h_n(0)]$ is beschränktartige. We have

$$\frac{1}{2\pi} \int\limits_0^{2\pi} e^{ipt}[h_n^{-1}(e^{it})]'e^{it}\,dt = \frac{1}{2\pi i} \int\limits_0^{2\pi} e^{ipt}\,dh_n^{-1}(e^{it})$$

$$= \frac{-p}{2\pi} \int\limits_0^{2\pi} h_n^{-1}(e^{it})e^{ipt}\,dt = \begin{cases} 0 & \text{if } p > 0, \\ qb_q & \text{if } q = -p, \end{cases}$$

where

$$b_q = \frac{1}{2\pi} \int\limits_0^{2\pi} h_n^{-1}(e^{it})e^{-iqt}\,dt.$$

Thus we get by Theorem 3.8 that

$$\lim_{r \to 1} \sum_{p=0} pb_p r^p e^{ipt} = [h_n^{-1}(e^{it})]'e^{it},$$

and that

$$\sum_{p=0}^{\infty} pb_p r^p e^{ipt}$$

belongs to $H_1(0,2\pi)$ (and hence is beschränktartige). But

$$\sum_{p=0}^{\infty} pb_p r^p e^{ipt} = z\frac{d}{dz}\left(\sum_{p=0}^{\infty} b_p z^p\right) = z\frac{d}{dz}h_n^{-1}(z),$$

and so (6.6a) holds. That $z(d/dz)h_n^{-1}(z)/[h_n^{-1}(z) - h_n(0)]$ is beschränktartige follows from the fact that it is the quotient of two beschränktartige functions.

We now finish the proof of the theorem. It follows that

$$\lim_{r\to 1} F_n(re^{it})\frac{z(d/dz)h_n^{-1}(z)}{h_n^{-1}(z) - h_n^{-1}(0)} = a_n(t) \text{ a.e.}$$

Moreover,

$$F_n(z)\frac{z(d/dz)h_n^{-1}(z)}{h_n^{-1}(z) - h_n^{-1}(0)}$$

is beschränktartige, being the product of two such functions, and has the same almost-everywhere radial limit as does the beschränktartige function $A_n(z)$. It follows from the uniqueness theorem for beschränktartige functions that for z in U,

$$A_n(z) = F_n(z)\frac{z(d/dz)h_n^{-1}(z)}{h_n^{-1}(z) - h_n^{-1}(0)} = F_n(z)\left[\frac{d}{dz}h_n^{-1}(z)\right]\left\{\frac{h_n^{-1}(z) - h_n^{-1}(0)}{z}\right\}^{-1}.$$

We note that $A_n(0) = F_n(0)$, since

$$\lim_{r\to 0}\left[\frac{d}{dz}h_n^{-1}(z)\right]\left\{\frac{h_n^{-1}(z) - h_n^{-1}(0)}{z}\right\}^{-1} = 1.$$

Therefore,

$$|A_n(0)| = |F_n(0)| = \left|\lim_{r\to 1}\frac{1}{2\pi}\int_0^{2\pi} F_n(re^{it})\,dt\right|$$

$$= \left|\frac{1}{2\pi}\int_0^{2\pi} [f(g^{-1}(h_n^{-1}(e^{it}))) - f(z_0)]\,dt\right|.$$

The last equality holds since F_n is an $H_1(0,2\pi)$ function.

Let $\varepsilon > 0$ be given. For n sufficiently large, the integrand in the last expression is less than ε in absolute value and, consequently,

$$|A_n(0)| < \varepsilon.$$

This gives

$$\left| \int_C \theta(s)dg(s) \right| = \left| \int_{C_n} \theta(s)dg(s) \right| = |A_n(0)| < \varepsilon,$$

from which we conclude that $\int_C \theta(s)dg(s) = 0$. But, this is the same as

$$f(z_0) = \frac{f(z_0)}{2\pi i} \int_C \frac{dg(s)}{g(s) - g(z_0)} = \frac{1}{2\pi i} \int_C \frac{f(s)dg(s)}{g(s) - g(z_0)}.$$

Corollary 6.6.1

If f, g, and D are as in Theorem 6.1, then we can represent f as a power series in $g - g(z_0)$,

$$f(z) = \sum_{n=0}^{\infty} a_n[g(z) - g(z_0)]^n,$$

for z in some neighborhood of z_0.

Theorem 6.7

If g is one-to-one in a neighborhood of z_0 that is contained in U, then there is a circular neighborhood D about z_0 such that $A(g;D)$ is an algebra.

Proof. Let D be any circular neighborhood centered at z_0, such that g is one-to-one on $\bar{D}$. Let f be an arbitrary function in $A(g;D)$. $A(g;D)$ is an algebra by Corollary 6.6.1.

We suggest that the reader study the proof of Theorem 6.6 from the point of view of generalizations of Theorem 3.9.

Chapter 7

TOPOLOGY OF
POINTWISE CONVERGENCE

In this chapter we shall use some of Walsh's polynomial approximation theory to study the geometric structure of sets in the complex plane that are associated with pointwise-convergent sequences of analytic functions or, more generally, sequences of light open maps. Our point of departure for this study comes from the existence of an entire analytic function, say f, such that $f(z) \to 0$ as $z \to \infty$ along any ray; more generally, $\lim f(z)$ exists as $z \to \infty$ along any ray, but the limit does not exist in a uniform manner (cf. [63], p. 212).

If f is such an entire function and we set $f_n(z) = f(nz)$, $n = 1,2,\ldots$, then $\{f_n\}_{n=1}^{\infty}$ is a pointwise-convergent sequence of analytic functions on the unit disc U. Since $\lim_n f_n$ cannot exist uniformly, there exists a point z_0 in U such that the sequence $\{f_n\}_{n=1}^{\infty}$ is not uniformly bounded on any neighborhood of z_0. We denote the collection of all such points by E and call E the exceptional set for the sequence $\{f_n\}_{n=1}^{\infty}$. Our problem is to characterize all sets E that arise in this manner.

Certain properties of the set E are immediately apparent. For example, $U - E$ is open and dense in U; every component of E must, so to speak, reach the boundary of U; and, finally measure–theoretic (area) arguments cannot be used in intrinsically characterizing E. In fact, for $\varepsilon > 0$, we can use a thick Cantor set on the circle and an example due to Malmquist (cf. [48]) to construct a pointwise convergent sequence of analytic functions with an exceptional set E such that $m(E) > \pi - \varepsilon$, where $m(E)$ denotes the planar Lebesgue measure.

The problem we are interested in is sometimes referred to as the *Montel problem* (cf. [53]) and its solution has appeared in the literature ([26], [42], and [51]). Our presentation is taken from Chapter IV of [44]. For the basic topology involved in this problem the reader is referred to [55].

Let K denote the complex numbers and ω the positive integers. For $r > 0$, let U_r denote the interior of the circle C_r with center 0 and radius r. We shall write U for U_1 and C for C_1. For $z \in K$, let $P_x(z)$ denote the real part of z and $P_y(z)$ the imaginary part of z. For $r > 0$ and $z \in K$, let $P_r(z) = z$ if $|z| \leq r$, and $P_r(z) = rz/|z|$ if $|z| > r$. Let I denote the interval $[0,1]$, and let Q denote $I \times I$. If M and N are subsets of K, we let $\delta(M,N)$ denote $\sup_{x \in M, y \in N} |x - y|$.

Let M be a compact set. By the interior $I(M)$ of M we shall mean the union of the bounded components of $K - M$. By the exterior $E(M)$ of M we shall mean the unbounded component of $K - M$. By the outer boundary $B(M)$ of M, we shall mean the set $\overline{E(M)} - E(M)$.

Definition 7.1. Let $E \subseteq M \subseteq S$ be subsets of K and F be a collection of functions defined on S. E is called the *exceptional set* of F with respect to M, if E is the set of all points $x \in M$ such that $U_{f \in F} f(V \cap S)$ is unbounded for all open sets V containing x. We shall write $E = E(F,M)$.

Lemma 7.1

Let M be a compact set and f a continuous function on $H = M \cup I(M)$ into K, such that f is an open map on $I(M)$. Then for $x \in I(M)$,

$$|f(x)| < \sup_{t \in M} |f(t)|.$$

Proof. We observe that since H is compact, $f(H)$ is compact. Since $f[I(M)]$ is open in K, the lemma follows trivially.

If g is a nonconstant differentiable function defined on a connected open set containing H, then g is an open map and hence Lemma 7.1 applies to g.

Theorem 7.2

Let A be an arc with end points i and y, such that $A - \{i\} \subseteq U$. Then if $\varepsilon > 0$, $\delta > 0$, $N > 0$, and $v > 1$, there exists a polynomial P and a point $t \in U_v$ such that $\delta[P_1(z),A] > \delta$ implies $|P(z)| < \varepsilon$ for all $z \in U_v$, $|t - y| < \delta$, and $|P(t)| > N$.

Proof. Let $r > v$, $W = A \cup [i,ir]$, and h be a homeomorphism of $\overline{U}$ onto $\overline{U}_r$, such that $h([0,i]) = W$, where for $v,w \in K$, $[v,w]$ denotes the line segment with end points v and w. The function h may be obtained by extending W to an arc W_0 intersecting $\overline{U}_r$ in exactly two points. To simplify topological considerations, one may consider all arcs mentioned to be polygonal.

Now $h^{-1}(\overline{U}_v)$ is a compact subset of U, and hence there exists $0 < r_0 < 1$ such that $h^{-1}(\overline{U}_v) \subseteq \overline{U}_{r_0}$. Since h is uniformly continuous, there exists $w > 0$, $w < r_0/2$, such that $|u - v| \leq w$ implies $|h(u) - h(w)| < \delta$ for all $u,v \in \overline{U}$. Let $x_1 = -w + i\sqrt{r_0^2 - w^2}$, $x_2 = -w$, $x_3 = i$, $x_4 = w - w^2 + iw$, $x_5 = w$, and $x_6 = w + i\sqrt{r_0^2 - w^2}$. Let G_0 be the subarc of C_{r_0} with end points x_1 and x_6 not containing ir_0 and G the simple closed curve $G_0 \cup_{i=1}^{5} [x_1,x_{i+1}]$. Clearly $x_0 = i(1 + r_0)/2$ lies in $I(G)$.

Let g be a map of $h(G)$ such that $g(z) = 0$ for all $z \in h(G) - h([x_4,x_5])$ and $|g(a)| > 2$ for some point $a \in h([x_4,x_5])$. From Theorem 6.05 there exists a differentiable function f on $K - \{h(x_0)\}$ such that $|f(x) - g(x)| < 1$ for all $x \in h(G)$. Then $|f(x)| < 1$ for all $x \in h(G) - h([x_4,x_5])$ and $|f(a)| > 1$.

If $m = -w + iw$, $n = w + iw$, $G_1 = G_0 \cup [x_1,x_2] \cup [x_2,x_5] \cup [x_5,x_6]$, and $G_2 = G_0 \cup [x_1,m] \cup [m,n] \cup [n,x_6]$, then $G_1 \subseteq \overline{I(G_2)}$ and $x_0 \notin \overline{I(G_2)}$. If $M_1 = \sup_{x \in h[\overline{I(G_1)}]} |f(x)|$ and $M_2 = \sup_{x \in h[\overline{I(G_2)}]} |f(x)|$, then, from Lemma 7.1, there exist $b \in h(G_1)$ and $t \in h(G_2)$ such that $|f(b)| = M_1$ and $|f(t)| = M_2$. Now $a \in I[h(G_2)]$, and hence $|f(t)| > |f(a)| > 1$. Consequently, $t \in h([m,n])$.

Suppose $M_1 \geq M_2$. Then $|f(b)| > 1$, and hence $b \in h([x_2,x_5]) \subseteq I[h(G_2)]$. But then $M_1 = |f(b)| < |f(t)| = M_2$. Thus $M_1 < M_2$. If for $x \in U_r$, $f_0(x) = 2f(x)/(M_1 + M_2)$, then $|f_0(x)| \leq 2M_1/(M_1 + M_2) < 1$ for all $x \in h[\overline{I(G_1)}]$ and $|f_0(t)| > 1$. There exists $n \in \omega$ such that $|f_0(t)|^2 > N + \varepsilon/2$ and $|f_0(x)|^n < \varepsilon/2$ for all $x \in h[\overline{I(G_1)}]$.

There exists a polynomial P such that $|P(x) - f_0(x)^n| < \varepsilon/2$ for all $x \in U_v$. If x is a point of U_v such that $\delta(P_1(x),A) \geq \delta$, then $\delta(x,W) \geq \delta$ and $h^{-1}(x) \in \overline{U}_{r_0}$. Now if $\delta[h^{-1}(x), [0,ir_0]] \leq w$, then $\delta(x,A) < \delta$. Thus $x \in h[\overline{I(G_1)}]$, $|f_0(x)^n| < \varepsilon/2$, and consequently $|P(x)| < \varepsilon$. Since $|P(t)| > N$, P is the desired polynomial.

Theorem 7.2a

Let $E \subseteq \overline{U}$. Then the following statements are equivalent:

(1) $E = E(F,\overline{U})$ for some pointwise-bounded collection F of open maps of a set S containing $\overline{U}$.

(2) E is such that:

    (a) E is compact.

    (b) Each component of E intersects C.

    (c) There exists a sequence $S_1 \supseteq S_2 \supseteq \cdots$ of open sets such that $\cap_1^\infty S_n = \emptyset$, and $E - S_n$ is its own outer boundary for $n \in \omega$.

(3) There exists a sequence of polynomials $P = \{P_n\}_{n=1}^{\infty}$ such that $\{P_n^{(p)}(z)\}_{n=1}^{\infty}$ converges to 0 for all $z \in \overline{U}$, $p = 0,1,\ldots$, and such that $E = E(P,\overline{U})$.

Proof. We first prove that (1) implies (2). Since $\overline{U}$ is closed, E is closed. Suppose M is a component of E such that $M \subseteq U$. Then, from the Zoretti theorem (cf. [96]), there exists a simple closed curve G such that $M \subseteq I(G)$, $\delta(x,M) < \delta(M,C)$ for all $x \in G$, and $G \cap E = \emptyset$. Hence $G \subseteq U$. Since $I(G)$ contains a point of E, we have that $U_{f \in F} f[I(G)]$ is unbounded. But then by Lemma 7.1, $U_{f \in F} f(G)$ is unbounded, and consequently G contains a point of E. Thus all components of E intersect C.

Let $n \in \omega$, and let $S_n' = \{x \in \overline{U} : |f(x)| > n$ for some $f \in F\}$. Since all elements of F are continuous, S_n' is open in the relative topology of $\overline{U}$. Hence $S_n' = S_n'' \cap \overline{U}$ for some open set S_n'' in K. Let $S_n = S_n'' \cap U_{1-1/n}$. Trivially $S_{n+1} \subseteq S_n$ for $n \in \omega$.

If $x \in \overline{U}$, there exists $M_x > 0$ such that $|f(x)| < M_x$ for all $f \in F$. Thus $x \notin S_n$ for all $n > M_x$, $n \in \omega$, and consequently $\cap_{n=1}^{\infty} S_n = \emptyset$. Let $n \in \omega$, and let $B = B(E - S_n)$. Suppose $B \neq E - S_n$ and let $x \in [E - S_n] - B$. Then $x \in I(B)$. Since $x \in E$, there exists $y \in I(B)$ and $f \in F$ such that $|f(y)| > n$. From Lemma 7.1 there exists $z \in B$ such that $|f(z)| > |f(y)| \geq n$. But then $z \in S_n$. Thus $B = E - S_n$.

We now show that (2) implies (3). Let X be a dense countable subset of E, and let $\{x_n\}_{n=1}^{\infty}$ be a sequence in X such that every element of X appears infinitely many times as a term of $\{x_n\}_{n=1}^{\infty}$. For $n \in \omega$, there exists a point y_n of $E(E - S_n)$ such that $|x_n - y_n| < \varepsilon/4$, where $\varepsilon = 1/2^n$. There exists an arc A with end points x and y_n such that $x \in C$, $A - \{x\} \subseteq U$, and $A \cap (E - S_n) = \emptyset$. From the Zoretti theorem there exists a simple closed curve G such that the component M of E containing x lies in $I(G)$, $G \cap E = \emptyset$, and $\delta(z,M) < \varepsilon/2$ for all $z \in G$. Since M intersects C, G must intersect C. Now $A \cap G = \emptyset$, or $A \cap G \neq \emptyset$, and there exists an arc A_0 in $A \cup G$ with end points y and z such that $z \in C$ and $A_0 - \{z\} \subseteq U$. Thus there exists an arc A with end points y_n and z_n such that $z_n \in C$ and $A_n - \{z_n\} \subseteq U$, $\delta(x,E) < \varepsilon/2$ for all $x \in A_n$, and such that $A_n \cap (E - S_n) = \emptyset$.

Suppose $\varepsilon_0 > 0$ and $\varepsilon_0 < 2^{-1} \inf\{1,\varepsilon,\delta(E - S_n,A_n)\}$. From Theorem 6.05 there exists a polynomial P_n and a point $t_n \in U_2 - (E - S_n)$ such that $|t_n - y_n| < \varepsilon_0$, $|P_n(t_n)| > n$, and such that $|P_n(z)| < \varepsilon_0^{n+1}/n!$ for all $z \in U_2$ for which $\delta[P_1(z),P_n] > \varepsilon_0$.

Now for $z \in E - S_n$, we have $\delta(z,A_n) > \varepsilon - \sup\{\delta(A_n,y)|y \in E - S_n\} \geq \varepsilon - \varepsilon/2 > \varepsilon_0$. Let $V_n = \{x \in U_2 | x \in E - S_n$ or $\delta[P_1(x),E - S_n] > \varepsilon\}$. Then for $z \in V_n$, $\delta[P_1(z),A_n] > \varepsilon_0$, and hence $|P_n(z)| < \varepsilon_0^{n+1}/n!$ Consequently,

$$|f_n^{(p)}(x)| = |p!(2\pi i)^{-1} \int_{D_x} f_n(z)(z-x)^{-p-1} dz|$$
$$\leq p!(2\pi i)^{-1}[2\pi\varepsilon_0] \inf_{z \in D_x} |f_n(z)|/\varepsilon_0^{p+1}$$
$$< p!\varepsilon_0^{-p}[\varepsilon_0^{n+1}/n!]$$
$$< \varepsilon_0 < \varepsilon = 1/2^n,$$

for $x \in \bar{U} \cap V_n$ and $p = 0,1,\ldots,n$, where D_x is the circle with center x and radius ε_0.

Let $x \in \bar{U} - E$ and $p = 0,1,\ldots L_x$ denote the interior of the circle with center x and radius $\delta(x,E)/3$. There exists $N > p$ such that $n > N$, $n \in \omega$, implies $2^{-n} < \delta(x,E)/2$, and thus

$$\delta[P_1(y),E - S_n] \geq \delta[P_1(y),E] > \delta(x,E) - \delta(x,E)/3 > 1/2^n,$$

for all $y \in L_x$. Thus for $n > N$, $n \in \omega$, $L_x \cap \bar{U} \subseteq V_n$, and consequently $|P_n^{(p)}(z)| < 1/2^n$ for all $z \in L_x$. Thus $x \notin E(P,\bar{U})$, where P denotes $\{P_n\}_{n=1}^\infty$. Let $x \in E$ and $p = 0,1,\ldots$. Then there exists $N > p$ such that $n > N$, $n \in \omega$, implies $x \in E - S_n$, and hence $x \in \bar{U} \cap V_n$; and consequently $|f_n^{(p)}(x)| < 1/2^n$.

Suppose again that $x \in E$. There exists $n_1 < n_2 < \cdots$ in ω such that $\{x_{n_i}\}_{i=1}^\infty$ converges to x. Now $\{t_{n_i} - x_{n_i}\}_{i=1}^\infty$ converges to zero, and $|P_{n_i}(t_{n_i})| > n_i$ for $i \in \omega$. Hence $\{t_{n_i}\}_{i=1}^\infty$ converges to x, and $x \in E(P,\bar{U})$. Thus $E = E(P,\bar{U})$, and P is the desired sequence of polynomials.

Remark. Say E is a compact subset of $\bar{U}$ satisfying (2c) of Theorem 7.2a. Then $E - S_n$ is the boundary of an open set in K and hence is nowhere dense in K, for $n \in \omega$. Thus $E = \bigcup_{n=1}^\infty E - S_n$ is the first category in K, and hence $K - E$ is dense in K. Since E is closed, $K - E$ is open, and hence E is nowhere dense in K.

Lemma 7.3

If $S_1 \supseteq S_2 \supseteq \cdots$ is a sequence of open sets in a compact metric space M such that $\bigcap_{n=1}^\infty S_n = \emptyset$, then $T = \bigcap_{n=1}^\infty \bar{S}_n$ is a compact nowhere-dense subset of M.

Proof. A subset V of M is a spherical region if there exists $x \in M$ and $\varepsilon > 0$ such that $V = \{y \in M | \delta(x,y) < \varepsilon\}$. Since M is a compact Hausdorff space, T must be compact.

Suppose that there exists a nonempty open set L such that $L \subseteq T$ and $n \in \omega$. Then $L \subseteq \bar{S}_n$. Thus $L \cap S_n$ is a nonempty open set, and hence there exists a spherical region V such that $\bar{V} \subseteq L \cap S_n \subseteq T \cap S_n$. Thus if T contains a nonempty open set L_0, we may define inductively a sequence $V_1,V_2,\ldots$ of spherical regions in T such that $\bar{V}_{n+1} \subseteq V_n \subseteq S_n$ for all $n \in \omega$.

But then $\bigcap_{n=1}^{\infty} V_n \neq \emptyset$, since M is a compact metric space, and $\bigcap_{n=1}^{\infty} V_n \subseteq \bigcap_{n=1}^{\infty} S_n = \emptyset$. Hence T is nowhere dense in M.

Theorem 7.3

Let E be a compact subset of K satisfying (2c) of Theorem 7.2a. Then for each closed nonempty subset $M \subseteq E$ there exists a compact subset T of M such that T is nowhere dense in the relative topology of M and such that if S is an open set in K containing T, then $M - S$ is its own outer boundary.

Proof. For $n \in \omega$, let $R_n = S_n \cap M$. Then R_n is open in the relative topology of M, $\bigcap_{n=1}^{\infty} R_n = \emptyset$, and $R_{n+1} \subseteq R_n$ for $n \in \omega$. Let $T = \bigcap_{n=1}^{\infty} \bar{R}_n$. Then from Lemma 7.3 T is a compact nowhere-dense subset of M.

Let S be an open set in K containing T. Then there exists $N > 0$ such that $n > N$, $n \in \omega$, implies $\bar{R}_n \subseteq S$, and hence

$$M - S \subseteq M - R_n \subseteq M - [S_n \cap M] = M - S_n \subseteq E - S_n.$$

Since $E - S_n = \bar{W}_n - W_n$, where $W_n = E(E - S_n)$, we have $M - S \subseteq E - S_n \subseteq \bar{W}_n - W_n$, and hence $M - S = B(M - S)$ for $n > N$, $n \in \omega$.

Remark. Theorem 7.3 is useful in excluding from our consideration certain sets with too much "fine" structure. In particular, we conclude from Theorem 7.3 that no exceptional set can contain the *universal plane curve* as a subset (cf. [1]).

Theorem 7.4

Let E_1 and E_2 be subsets of $\bar{U}$ satisfying (2) of Theorem 7.2a. Then $E = E_1 \cup E_2$ also satisfies (2).

Proof. From Theorem 7.2a there exist pointwise-bounded collections F_1 and F_2 of open maps of $\bar{U}$ into K such that $E_1 = E(F_1, \bar{U})$ and $E_2 = E(F_2, \bar{U})$. Let $x \in E - \bar{U}$. Then $x \notin E_1$ and $x \notin E_2$, and hence there exist open sets V_1 and V_2, and positive numbers M_1 and M_2, such that $x \in V_n$, and $|f(y)| < M_n$ for all $y \in V_n \cap \bar{U}, f \in F_n$, and $n = 1,2$. Then $|f(y)| < M_1 + M_2$ for $y \in (V_1 \cap V_2) \cap \bar{U}$ and $f \in F_1 \cup F_2 = F$, and consequently $x \notin E(F, \bar{U})$. Similarly, $E(F_1, \bar{U}) \cup E(F_2, \bar{U}) \subseteq E(F, \bar{U})$. Thus $E = E(F, \bar{U})$, and hence, from Theorem 7.2a, E satisfies (2).

Theorem 7.5

Let $x_0 \in U$ and E a subcontinuum of $\bar{U}$, irreducible between x_0 and C. Then E satisfies (2) of Theorem 7.2a.

Proof. Trivially E satisfies (2a) and (2b). Let $n \in \omega$, $S_n = \{z \in K | P_y(x_0) < P_y(z) < P_y(x_0) + 1/n\}$, and $B_n = B(E - S_n)$. Suppose $B_n \neq E - S_n$ and $x \in (E - S_n) - B_n$. Let R be the component of $I(B_n)$ containing x and D denote $B(R)$. Then $x \in I(D)$ and D is connected. Now by our construction $x_0 \in E(E - S_n) \supseteq B_n \supseteq D$. If H and K are subcontinua of E, such that H is irreducible between C and D, and K is irreducible between D and x_0, then $H \cup D \cup K$ is a subcontinuum of E, intersecting C, containing x_0, and excluding x. From the irreducibility of E, we have $E = H \cup D \cup K$. But then $x \notin E$. Thus $B_n = E - S_n$, and consequently E satisfies (2c).

Theorem 7.6

If $E \subseteq U$, then the following statements are equivalent:

(1) $E = E(F,U)$ for some pointwise-bounded collection F of open maps of U into K.

(2) Each component of $\bar{E}$ intersects C and E is closed in the relative topology of U.

(3) There exists a sequence $P = \{P_n\}_{n=1}^{\infty}$ of polynomials such that $E = E(P,U)$, and $\{P_n^{(p)}(z)\}_{n=1}^{\infty}$ converges to zero for all $x \in \bar{U}$ and $p = 0,1,\ldots$.

Proof. We first show that (1) implies (2). Let $x \in U$. Then for $|x| < r < 1$, $x \in E(F,\bar{U}_r) \subseteq E$, and hence from Theorem 7.2a there exists a subcontinuum M_r of $E(F,\bar{U}_r)$ containing x and intersecting C_r. Then $M = U_{|x| < r < 1} M_r$ is a connected set containing x such that $\bar{M}$ intersects C. Thus $\bar{E}$ satisfies (2b) of Theorem 7.2a.

Let $x_0 \in \bar{E} \cap C$. For $n \in \omega$, set $R_n = \{x \in U | |f(x)| > n$ for some $f \in F\}$. Then $R_{n+1} \subseteq R_n$, R_n is open, and $\cap_{i=1}^{\infty} R_i = \emptyset$. Let

$$S_n = R_n \cup (U - \bar{U}_{1 - 1/n}) \cup (L_n - \{x_0\}),$$

where L_n is the interior of the circle with center x_0 and radius $1/n$. Now S_n is open, $S_{n+1} \subseteq S_n$, and $\cap_{i=1}^{\infty} S_i = \emptyset$. Now for $n \in \omega$, $\bar{E} - S_n - C = \bar{E} \cap \bar{U}_{1 - 1/n} - R_n = E(F,\bar{U}_{1 - 1/n}) - R_n$, and hence $\bar{E} - S_n - C$ is its own outer boundary. Then clearly $E - S_n = B(E - S_n)$, and thus $\bar{E}$ satisfies (2c) of Theorem 7.2a. Trivially E is closed in the relative topology of U.

The proof that (2) implies (3) follows readily from Theorem 7.2a. The proof that (3) implies (1) is trivial.

Theorem 7.7

Let E be a closed subset of K. Then the following four statements are equivalent:

(1) $E = E(F,K)$ for some pointwise-bounded collection F of open maps of K into K.

(2) E is such that:

    (a) Each component of E is unbounded.

    (b) There exists a sequence of open sets $S_1 \supseteq S_2 \supseteq \cdots$ such that for $n \in \omega$, $E - S_n$ is its own outer boundary (we here define the outer boundary of a closed but not bounded set as the boundary of the union of the unbounded components of its complement), and such that $\bigcap_{i=1}^{\infty} S_i = \emptyset$.

(3) E is such that:

    (a) For $r > 0$, all components of $E \cap \overline{U}_r$ intersect C_r.

    (b) There exists a sequence of open sets $S_1, S_2, \ldots$ such that for $r > 0$, $(E \cap \overline{U}_r) - S_n$ is its own outer boundary, and $\bigcap_{i=1}^{\infty} S_i = \emptyset$.

(4) There exists a sequence of polynomials $P = \{P_n\}_{n=1}^{\infty}$ such that $E = E(P,K)$, and $\{P_n^{(p)}(z)\}_{n=1}^{\infty}$ converges to 0, for $z \in K$, and $p = 0,1,\ldots$.

Proof. We first show that (1) implies (2). Let $x \in K$. Then for $r > |x|$, $x \in E(F,\overline{U}) \subseteq E$, and hence from Theorem 7.2a there exists a subcontinuum M_r of $E(F,\overline{U}_r)$ containing x and intersecting C_r. Then $M = U_{r>|x|}M_r$ is an unbounded connected subset of E containing x. Thus E satisfies (2b).

For $n \in \omega$, let $S_n = \{x \in K : |f(x)| > n$ for some $f \in F\}$. Then for $n \in \omega$, $S_{n+1} \subseteq S_n$, S_n is open, and $\bigcap_{i=1}^{\infty} S_i = \emptyset$. Let $B = B(E - S_n)$. Suppose $B \neq E - S_n$ and $x \in (E - S_n) - B$. If R is the component of $I(B)$ containing x, then R is bounded. Now $U_{f \in F} f(R)$ must be unbounded. Hence by Lemma 7.1 there exist $y \in \overline{R} - R \subseteq B$ and $f \in F$ such that $|f(y)| > n$. But then $y \in S_n$. Thus $B = E - S_n$ and E satisfies (2b).

The proof that (2) implies (3) is obvious. The sequence $S_1 \supseteq S_2 \supseteq \cdots$ defined clearly satisfies (3b).

We now show that (3) implies (4). Let X be a countable dense subset of E and let $\{x_n\}_{n=1}^{\infty}$ be a sequence in X such that every element of X appears infinitely many times as a term of $\{x_n\}_{n=1}^{\infty}$. Let $0 < r_1 < r_2 < \cdots$ be a sequence of numbers such that $x_n \in U_{r_n}$ for $n \in \omega$. Then $\sup_{n \in \omega} r_n = \infty$. From the proof of Theorem 7.2a, for $n \in \omega$, there exist a polynomial P_n and a point $t_n \in K$ such that $|f_n^{(p)}(z)| < 1/2^n$ for $p = 0,1,\ldots,n$, and $x \in \overline{U}_{r_{n+1}}$ such that $x \in (E \cap \overline{U}_{r_n}) - S_n$ or $\delta[P_{r_n}(x), E \cap \overline{U}_{r_n}] > 1/2^n$, and such that $|P_n(t_n)| > n$ and $|t_n - x_n| < 1/2^n$.

Let $n \in \omega$ and $\{y_i\}_{i=1}^{\infty}$ be the subsequence of $\{x_i\}_{i=1}^{\infty}$ consisting of all terms of $\{x_i\}_{i=1}^{\infty}$ lying in $\overline{U}_n$. Then $\{y_i\}_{i=1}^{\infty}$ is dense in $E_n = E \cap \overline{U}_n$. Using arguments identical to the arguments in the proof of Theorem 7.2a, it follows that $E_n = E(P,\overline{U}_n)$, and that $\{P_i^{(p)}(z)\}_{i=1}^{\infty}$ converges to 0 for all $x \in \overline{U}_n$ and $p = 0,1,\ldots$. Now $E = U_{n=1}^{\infty} E_n$ and hence $E = E(P,K)$, and thus E satisfies (4).

The proof that (4) implies (1) is trivial.

Remark. Let $F = \{f_n\}_{n=1}^{\infty}$ be a sequence of differentiable functions on U, converging pointwise to 0 on U, and let $G = \{f'_n\}_{n=1}^{\infty}$. Then it may be readily shown that $E(F,U) = E(G,U)$. However, it is not necessarily true that G is pointwise-bounded on U. We shall now construct an example of such a sequence.

For $n \in \omega$, let $A_n = [-2,0] \cup [0,i/2^n]$. Then from Theorem 6.05 there exists a polynomial P_n and a point $t_n \in U_2$ such that $|P_n(z)| < \frac{1}{2}^{2n}$ for all $z \in U_2$, such that $\delta(z,A_n) > \frac{1}{2}^{2n}$, and such that $|P_n(t_n)| > n$, and

$$|t_n - i/2^{2n}| < \frac{1}{2}^{2n}.$$

Now there exists $x_n \in U_2$ such that $|P_n(z)| < \frac{1}{2}^n$ for all $z \in U_2$, such that $P_y(z) > P_y(x_n)$, and such that $|P_n(x_n)| = \frac{1}{2}^n$. Clearly $P_y(x_n) \geq 2^{-n} - 2^{-2n}$, and hence $\delta([-2,0],x_n) > \frac{1}{2}^{2n}$. Thus we must have $|x_n - i/2^n| < \frac{1}{2}^{2n}$. Clearly $P_y(x_n) < 2^{-n} + 2^{-2n}$.

Let y_n be a point of U_2 such that $P_x(y_n) = P_x(x_n)$ and $P_y(y_n) = 2^{-n} + 2^{-2n}$. Then $|P_n(y_n)| < \frac{1}{2}^{2n}$. Now $0 < |x_n - y_n| \leq 2/2^{2n}$, and

$$|P_n(x_n) - P_n(y_n)| \geq |P_n(x_n)| - |P_n(y_n)| = 2^{-n} - |P_n(y_n)| > 2^{-n} - 2^{-2n}.$$

By the mean-value theorem for real-valued functions there exists $s_n \in U_2$ such that $P_y(x_n) < P_y(s_n) < P_y(y_n)$, and $|P'_n(s_n)| \geq 2^{-1}|P_n(x_n) - P_n(y_n)|$.

$$|x_n - y_n|^{-1} > [2^{-n} - 2^{-2n}][2/2^{2n}]^{-1} = 2^n(1 - 2^{-n}) \geq 2^{n-1}.$$

Now $|s_n - x_n| < 2/2^n$, and hence, since $|x_n - i/2^n| < \frac{1}{2}^{2n}$, we have

$$|s_n - i/2^n| < \frac{3}{2}^{2n}.$$

Since $P_y(s_n) > P_y(x_n)$, we have $|P_n(z)| < \frac{1}{2}^n$ for all $z \in U_2$ such that

$$P_y(z) \geq P_y(s_n).$$

For $n \in \omega$, let $Q_n(z) = P_n(z + s_n)$ for all $z \in K$. Then for $z \in \overline{U}$ we have $|Q_n(z)| < \frac{1}{2}^{2n}$ if $P_y(z) < P_y(s_n)$, a condition satisfied whenever $P_y(z) < 0$ or $P_y(z) > 2^{-n} + \frac{3}{2}^{2n}$, and we have $|Q_n(z)| < \frac{1}{2}^n$ whenever $P_y(z) > P_y(x_n) - P_y(s_n)$, where $P_y(x_n) - P_y(s_n) < 0$. It follows that $\{Q_n(z)\}_{n=1}^{\infty}$ converges to 0 for all $z \in \overline{U}$, and $\lim_{n\to\infty} |Q'_n(0)| = \infty$.

The extension of the results of this chapter to sequences of light open maps in higher-dimensional spaces remains an open problem.

Appendix A

THE FOURIER TRANSFORM

THERE ARE SEVERAL WAYS of obtaining the Plancherel theory for the Fourier transform. The method we have chosen, for the sake of brevity, hides the basic algebraic structure of the theory. For this structure we refer the reader to [58], [78], or [46].

The Plancherel theorem tells us that if $f \in L_2(-\infty,\infty)$, $a > 0$, and

$$h_a(x) = \frac{1}{\sqrt{2\pi}} \int_{-a}^{a} e^{ixy} f(y)\, dy, \qquad (A.1a)$$

then $\lim_{a\to\infty} h_a = h$ in the L_2 norm; moreover, if

$$f_a(y) = \frac{1}{\sqrt{2\pi}} \int_{-a}^{a} e^{-ixy} h(x)\, dx, \qquad (A.1b)$$

then $\lim_{a\to\infty} f_a = f$ in the L_2 norm.

To prove this, we set

$$a_v = \int_{v/\lambda}^{(v+1)/\lambda} f(x)\, dx \qquad v = 0, \pm 1, \pm 2, \ldots,$$

and

$$\Phi_n(x) = \sum_{v=-n}^{n} a_v e^{ivx/\lambda}.$$

If $b > 0$ and $n = [\lambda b] - 1$, then

$$\lim_{\lambda\to\infty} \Phi_n(x) = \int_{-b}^{b} f(y) e^{ixy}\, dy \qquad (A.1c)$$

135

uniformly on compact subsets of $(-\infty,\infty)$. Also,

$$|a_v|^2 \leq \frac{1}{\lambda} \int\limits_{v/\lambda}^{(v+1)/\lambda} |f(x)|^2 \, dx.$$

If $0 < \alpha \leq \pi\lambda$, then

$$\int\limits_{-\alpha}^{\alpha} |\Phi_n(x)|^2 \, dx \leq 2\pi\lambda \sum\limits_{v=-n}^{n} |a_v|^2 \leq 2\pi \int\limits_{-b}^{b} |f(x)|^2 \, dx. \qquad (A.1d)$$

Fixing α, allowing $\lambda \to \infty$, and using (A.1c) gives us

$$\int\limits_{-\alpha}^{\alpha} \left| \int\limits_{-b}^{b} f(y)e^{ixy} \, dy \right|^2 dx \leq 2\pi \int\limits_{-b}^{b} |f(x)|^2 \, dx;$$

therefore,

$$\int\limits_{-\infty}^{\infty} \left| \int\limits_{-b}^{b} f(y)e^{iyx} \, dy \right|^2 dx \leq (2\pi) \int\limits_{-b}^{b} |f(x)|^2 \, dx. \qquad (A.1e)$$

Inasmuch as (A.1e) is true for any $f \in L_2(-\infty,\infty)$, it follows that $\lim_{a\to\infty} h_a = h$ and

$$\int\limits_{-\infty}^{\infty} |h(x)|^2 \, dx \leq \int\limits_{-\infty}^{\infty} |f(x)|^2 \, dx. \qquad (A.1f)$$

If we reverse the role of f and h and set

$$f_a(x) = \frac{1}{\sqrt{2\pi}} \int\limits_{-a}^{a} h(y)e^{-iyx} \, dy,$$

then the same argument shows that $\lim_{a\to\infty} f_a = \varphi$ in the L_2 norm and we must show $\varphi = f$ a.e. To this end it is sufficient to show that

$$\int\limits_{0}^{t} \varphi(x) \, dx = \int\limits_{0}^{t} f(x) \, dx$$

for $-\infty < t < \infty$. But

$$\int\limits_{0}^{t} \varphi(x) \, dx = \lim_{a\to\infty} \frac{1}{\sqrt{2\pi}} \int\limits_{0}^{t} \left\{ \int\limits_{-a}^{a} h(y)e^{-ixy} \, dy \right\} dx$$

$$= \frac{1}{\sqrt{2\pi}} \int\limits_{-\infty}^{\infty} h(y) \frac{e^{-ity} - 1}{-iy} \, dy$$

by the Fubini theorem. Also,

$$\int_0^t f(x)\,dx = \frac{1}{\pi}\int_0^\infty y^{-1}\left\{\int_{-\infty}^\infty f(u)[\sin y(t-u) + \sin uy]\,du\right\}dy$$

$$= \frac{1}{\sqrt{2\pi}}\int_{-\infty}^\infty \frac{e^{-ity}-1}{iy}\left\{\int_{-\infty}^\infty f(u)e^{-iyu}\,du\right\}dy$$

$$= \frac{1}{\sqrt{2\pi}}\int_{-\infty}^\infty \frac{e^{-ity}-1}{iy}h(y)\,dy.$$

Thus $f = \varphi$ a.e., and (A.1f) gives us

$$\int_{-\infty}^\infty |f(x)|^2\,dx = \int_{-\infty}^\infty |h(x)|^2\,dx \qquad\qquad (A.1g)$$

upon changing the role of f and h.

For each $f \in L_2(-\infty,\infty)$, we set

$$\hat{f}(x) = \frac{1}{\sqrt{2\pi}}\int_{-\infty}^\infty e^{iyx}f(y)\,dy.$$

Since, the polar form for the inner product

$$4(f,h) = \|f+h\|^2 - \|f-h\|^2 + i\|f+ih\|^2 - i\|f-ih\|^2$$

holds in any Hilbert space, (A.1g) gives us

$$\int_{-\infty}^\infty f(x)\overline{h(x)}\,dx = \int_{-\infty}^\infty \hat{f}(y)\overline{\hat{h}(y)}\,dy$$

for every pair $f,h \in L_2(-\infty,\infty)$ with transforms f' and h', respectively.

The above presentation is taken from [88]. In the way of an additional application of the Plancherel theory, we shall develop some of the closure properties of the Hermite functions. These functions play an important role in many areas of analysis and have an extensive literature. Our arguments are taken from [56].

The theory of Hermite polynomials can be based on the defining formula

$$E(-t^2 + 2tx) = \sum_{n=0}^\infty t^n(n!)^{-1}H_n(x), \qquad\qquad (A.1h)$$

where H_n are the Hermite polynomials (not normalized) and $E(u) = e^u$. The completeness of the H_n in the Hilbert space **H** of functions f, for which

$$\|f\|^2 = \int_{-\infty}^{\infty} |f(x)|^2 E(-x^2)\, dx$$

exists, is usually reduced to the completeness of Laguerre polynomials or it is referred to the eigenfunction expansion for singular differential equations.

We shall give a short proof of the completeness of the H_n in $\mathbf{H}$ that goes through verbatum to the k-dimensional case by using (A.1h) directly and the Parseval identity for Fourier integrals. For the proof we note the orthogonal relations

$$\int_{-\infty}^{\infty} H_n(x)H_m(x)E(-x^2)\, dx = \sqrt{\pi}\, 2^n n!\, \delta_{nm}, \tag{A.1i}$$

which follow directly from (A.1h) by integrating

$$E(-t^2 + 2tx)E(-t^2 - 2tx).$$

Let f be a function in $\mathbf{H}$ for which

$$\int_{-\infty}^{\infty} f(x)H_n(x)E(-x^2)\,dx = 0, \tag{A.1j}$$

for $n = 0,1,\dots$. We shall show that f is the zero element in $\mathbf{H}$. Multiplying (A.1h) by $f(x)E(-x^2)$ and integrating, we obtain

$$\int_{-\infty}^{\infty} f(x)E(-(t-x)^2)\, dx$$

$$= \int_{-\infty}^{\infty} \sum_{n=0}^{N} t^n(n!)^{-1} H_n(x)f(x)E(-x^2)\, dx + R_N,$$

where

$$R_N = \int_{-\infty}^{\infty} \sum_{n>N} t^n(n!)^{-1} H_n(x)f(x)E(-x^2)\, dx$$

and can be estimated by Schwarz' inequality. Hence

$$|R_n|^2 \le \int_{-\infty}^{\infty} f(x)^2 E(-x^2)\, dx \int_{-\infty}^{\infty} \left\{ \sum_{n>N} t^n(n!)^{-1} H_n(x) \right\}^2 E(-x^2)\, dx,$$

which by (A.1i) yields

$$|R_N|^2 \le \|f\|^2 \sum_{n>N} t^{2n}(n!)^{-2}\sqrt{\pi 2^n(n!)}.$$

This series converges for all complex t, so that

$$\int_{-\infty}^{\infty} f(x)E(-(t-x)^2)\,dx = 0 \qquad\qquad (A.1k)$$

for all complex t. Multiplying (A.1k) by $E(t^2)$ and setting $t = is/2$, where s is real, we get

$$\int_{-\infty}^{\infty} f(x)E(-x^2)E(isx)\,dx = 0,$$

which, since $f(x)E(-x^2)$ belongs to L_2, gives us, by Parseval's formula,

$$\int_{-\infty}^{\infty} |f|^2 E(-2x^2)\,dx = 0,$$

which, in turn, is equivalent to

$$\int_{-\infty}^{\infty} |f|^2 E(-x^2)\,dx = 0,$$

so that f is the zero element in H.

For convergence discussions of the expansions of functions into Hermite polynomials, it is useful to have a crude estimate on H_n^*, $n = 0,1,\ldots,$ where

$$H_n^*(x) = \pi^{-1/4}2^{-n/2}(n!)^{-1/2}H_n(x) \qquad\qquad (A.1l)$$

and are the normalized Hermite polynomials. Expanding the left side of (A.1h) into the product of two power series and collecting the coefficients of the powers of t, we get

$$H_n(x)(n!)^{-1} = \sum_{p=0}^{n} c_p(-1)^{p/2}\left(\frac{p}{2}\right)^{-1}(2x)^{n-p}((n-p)!)^{-1},$$

where $c_p = 0$ or 1, according as to p being odd or even. Using, on the right side of (A.1l), $(2k!)^{-1/2} \le (k!)^{-1}$, multiplying and dividing $n!$, and Schwarz' inequality, we get

$$|H_n(x)|(n!)^{-1} \le (n!)^{-1/2}2^{n/2}E(2x^2),$$

so that

$$|H_n^*(x)| \leq \pi^{-1/4} E(2x^2).$$

We leave it to the reader to show that the normalized Hermite functions $H_n^*(x)$ are eigenfunctions (corresponding to the eigenvalues $(-i)^n$) for the Fourier transform on $L_2(-\infty,\infty)$.

Our final application of the Fourier transform concerns the extension of Theorem 3.9 to the case of the real line and the connection between this extension and the results of Lemma 1.6.1 to Theorem 1.7.

If φ is a normalized function of bounded variation on $(-\infty,\infty)$ such that $\varphi(-\infty) = 0$, then the Fourier transform φ^* of φ is defined by

$$\varphi^*(t) = \int_{-\infty}^{\infty} e^{iyt}\, d\varphi(y) \tag{A.1m}$$

for $-\infty \leq t \leq \infty$. Note that φ^* is a continuous function on $(-\infty,\infty)$. Also, in (A.1m) we have taken the $+$ sign instead of the usual $-$ sign in the exponential as a matter of convenience. We shall start with the following lemma.

Lemma A

If φ is a normalized function of bounded variation on $(-\infty,\infty)$ such that $\varphi(-\infty) = 0$, then

$$\int_{-\infty}^{\infty} \frac{1}{\xi + y}\, d\varphi(y) = 0 \tag{A.1n}$$

for $I_m \xi > 0$ if and only if $\varphi^*(t) = 0$ for $t > 0$.

Proof. If $\varphi^*(t) = 0$ for $t > 0$ and $R_e z > 0$, then

$$0 = \int_0^{\infty} e^{-zt}\varphi^*(t)\, dt = \int_0^{\infty} e^{-zt}\left\{\int_{-\infty}^{\infty} e^{iyt}\, d\varphi(y)\right\} dt \tag{A.1o}$$

$$0 = \int_{-\infty}^{\infty} \left\{\int_0^{\infty} e^{-(z-iy)t}\, dt\right\} d\varphi(y) = \int_{-\infty}^{\infty} \frac{1}{z - iy}\, d\varphi(y) \tag{A.1p}$$

$$0 = i \int_{-\infty}^{\infty} \frac{1}{iz + y}\, d\varphi(y) = i \int_{-\infty}^{\infty} \frac{1}{\xi + y}\, d\varphi(y), \tag{A.1q}$$

where $\xi = iz$ and the transition from (A.1n) to (A.1p) is allowable by the Fubini theorem. Inasmuch as all the above steps are reversible, the necessity follows from the uniqueness of the Laplace transform. The proof of the uniqueness of the Laplace transform is, in fact, a special case of Theorem 1.15; take $z = w + 1$ and

$$\Psi(t) = \int_0^t e^{-s}\varphi^*(s)\, ds,$$

so that

$$\int_0^\infty e^{-wt}\, d\Psi(t) = 0.$$

The class $H_1(I_m\xi > 0)$ is the set of all functions f such that f is analytic on $I_m\xi > 0$ and

$$\sup_y \int_{-\infty}^\infty |f(x + iy)|\, dx < \infty. \tag{A.1r}$$

The transformation $\xi = iz$, used to establish the equivalence of (A.1p) and (A.1q), allows us to translate all the results for $H_1(R_e z > 0)$ (cf. Lemma 1.6.1 to Theorem 1.7) to $H_1(I_m\xi > 0)$.

Theorem A

If φ is a normalized function of bounded variation on $(-\infty,\infty)$ such that $\varphi(-\infty) = 0$ and $\varphi^*(t) = 0$ for $t > 0$, then φ is absolutely continuous and there exists uniquely $f \in H_1(I_m\xi) > 0$ such that

$$\varphi'(t) = \lim_{s \to 0} \overline{f(-t + is)} \quad \text{a.e.}$$

Proof. Suppose $\varphi = \varphi_1 + i\varphi_2$ and

$$f_j(\xi) = \int_{-\infty}^\infty \frac{1}{\xi + y}\, d\varphi_j(y), \tag{A.1s}$$

$j = 1,2$. In view of our hypothesis on φ^* and the preceding lemma, $f_1 \equiv -if_2$. If $f_j = u_j + iv_j$, then $u_1 \equiv v_2$ and $u_2 \equiv -v_1$. If

$$-\infty < a < b < \infty$$

and φ_j is continuous at each of a and b, then upon integrating the imaginary part of (A.1s) and using the Fubini theorem, we get

$$\int_{-\infty}^\infty \left[\arctan \frac{b + y}{s} - \arctan \frac{a + y}{s} \right] d\varphi_j(y) = -\int_a^b v_j(t + is)\, dt. \tag{A.1t}$$

If we regard φ_j as a measure on each of $(-\infty,-b)$ and $(-b,\infty)$ and decompose the first term on the left side of (A.1t) into

$$\int_{-\infty}^{-b} \arctan \frac{b+y}{s} \, d\varphi_j(y) + \int_{-b}^{\infty} \arctan \frac{b+y}{s} \, d\varphi_j(y), \qquad \text{(A.1u)}$$

then (by the Lebesgue dominant convergence theorem), as $s \to 0$, (A.1t) approaches

$$\frac{-\pi}{2} \varphi_j(-b) + \frac{\pi}{2} [\varphi_j(\infty) - \varphi_j(-b)] = -\pi\varphi_j(-b) + \frac{\pi}{2}\varphi_j(\infty).$$

Similarly, the second term on the left side of (A.1t) approaches

$$\frac{-\pi}{2}\varphi_j(\infty) + \pi\varphi_j(-a)$$

or, what is the same,

$$\varphi_j(-b) - \varphi_j(-a) = \lim_{s\to 0} \frac{1}{\pi} \int_a^b v_j(t+is) \, dt, \qquad \text{(A.1v)}$$

which is essentially the Stieltjes inversion formula for the Stieltjes transform (cf. [92] or [97]). Inasmuch as φ_j is normalized and

$$\int_{-\infty}^{\infty} |d\varphi_j| < \infty,$$

and immediate consequence of (A.1v) is that $v_j(t+is) \in L_1(-\infty,\infty)$ for every s and

$$\lim_{s\to 0} \frac{1}{\pi} \int_{-\infty}^{\infty} |v_j(t+is)| \, dt = \int_{-\infty}^{\infty} |d\varphi_j|. \qquad \text{(A.1w)}$$

An argument exactly like the one used in the proof of Lemma 1.6.3 gives us that

$$\lim_{s\to 0} v_j(b+is) = \pi\varphi_j'(-b) \, \text{a.e.} \qquad \text{(A.1x)}$$

Hence, $v_j(t+is)$ approaches a measurable function $\varphi'(t)$ as $s \to 0$ and, moreover, in virtue of (A.1w) and Fatou's lemma, $\varphi_j'(t) \in L_1(-\infty,\infty)$. Since $v_1 \equiv -u_2$ and $v_2 \equiv u_1$, $f_j \in H_1(I_m\xi > 0)$ and $f_j(t+is)$ approaches a function, say, $F_j(t) \in L_1(-\infty,\infty)$. If we set $f = -if_1\pi$, then we get the desired conclusion, and this concludes our proof of the theorem.

We shall now restate the preceding theorem in a form more compatible with Theorem 3.9.

Corollary.

If Ψ is a normalized function of bounded variation on $(-\infty,\infty)$ such that $\Psi(-\infty) = 0$ and

$$\int_{-\infty}^{\infty} e^{-iyt}\, d\Psi(t) = 0$$

for $t < 0$, then Ψ is absolutely continuous and there exists uniquely $f \in H(I_m\xi > 0)$ such that

$$\Psi'(t) = \lim_{s \to 0} f(t + is)\, \text{a.e.}$$

Proof. Let $\varphi(y) = \overline{\Psi(\infty)} - \overline{\Psi(-y)}$ and use the preceding theorem.

There is a partial generalization to Theorem 3.10. The difficulty in this direction lies in defining the Fourier transform for functions $F \in L_p(-\infty,\infty)]2 < p$. The case $p = 2$ and $p = 1$ are covered equations (A.1a) and (A.1m), respectively; (in A.1m) replace $d\varphi(y)$ by $\varphi'(y)\,dy$. For $1 < p < 2$, $F \in L_p(-\infty,\infty)$, and F a simple function, we define the Fourier transform F^* of F by

$$F^*(t) = \frac{1}{\sqrt{2\pi}} \int_{-\infty}^{\infty} e^{ist} F(s)\, ds,$$

and then appeal to the convexity theorem of M. Riesz and Thorin (cf. [98], Vol. II, pp. 95, 254) and extend the transform to all of $L_p(-\infty,\infty)$. Once this is done, $F^*(t)$ makes sense for every $F \in L_p(-\infty,\infty)$, $1 < p < 2$, $F^* \in L_q(-\infty,\infty)$, $\|F^*\|_q \leq (\sqrt{2\pi})^{1-2/p}\|F\|_p$, and we have the reciprocal relation

$$F(s) = \frac{1}{\sqrt{2\pi}} \int_{-\infty}^{\infty} F^*(t)e^{-ist}\, dt$$

where the latter integral converges to F in the norm of $L_p(-\infty,\infty)$. Hence, assuming the transform has been defined for $L_p(-\infty,\infty)$, $1 < p < 2$, and taking a $F \in L_p(-\infty,\infty)$ such that $F^*(t) = 0$ for $t > 0$, then, arguing as in the case of Lemma A, we arrive at the following variation of (A.1n):

$$0 = \int_{-\infty}^{\infty} \frac{1}{\xi + y} F(y)\, dy$$

for $I_m \xi > 0$. At this stage we either repeat our technique and show directly that F is the conjugate limit of a function in $H_p(I_m \xi > 0)$ or, by use of partial fractions, replace the above equation by

$$0 = \int_{-\infty}^{\infty} \frac{1}{\xi + y} \frac{1}{\xi_0 + y} F(y) \, dy,$$

$I_m \xi_0 > 0$, ξ_0 fixed, and appeal to the case $p = 1$, $p = 2$, or Theorem A.

The failure of Theorem 3.10 to extend beyond the cases $p \le 2$ indicates that there is some delicacy and difficulty involved in using conformal mapping to obtain the full H_p theory for half-planes from the corresponding theory for the unit disc. Part of this difficulty is associated with the Fourier transform, and part of it is associated with the Poisson integral formula which does not extend to, say, rectangular curves in the half-plane.

The preceding paragraph amounts to a partial explanation of why we developed our H_p theory de novo.

Appendix B

INFINITE SYSTEMS
OF EQUATIONS IN HILBERT SPACE

SUPPOSE $\mathcal{H}$ IS a separable Hilbert space $A_n = \{a_{nm}\}_{m=1}^\infty$, $n = 1,2,\ldots$, and $\{\beta_i\}_{i=1}^\infty$ is a sequence of numbers. We shall establish conditions under which the infinite system of linear equations

$$\sum_{m=1}^\infty a_{nm}x_m = \beta_n, \qquad n = 1,2,\ldots \tag{B.1a}$$

has a solution $X = \{x_m\}_{m=1}^\infty \in \mathcal{H}$. If X^* denotes $\{\bar{x}_m\}_{m=1}^\infty$, then (B.1a) becomes

$$(A_n, X^*) = \beta_n, \qquad n = 1,2,\ldots. \tag{B.1b}$$

Before establishing the main theorem let us discuss the question of uniqueness. If the system (B.1b) has a solution, then a necessary and sufficient condition for the solution to be unique is that the set $\{A_n\}_{n=1}^\infty$ be fundamental in $\mathcal{H}$. The necessity is obvious and for the sufficiency let H denote the closed subspace generated by $\{A_n\}_{n=1}^\infty$. Hence $\mathcal{H} = H + H^\perp$. Consequently, if $Z \in H^\perp$ and X is a solution of (B.1b), then so is $X + Z$. Also, if $Y \in \mathcal{H}$, $Y = X + Z$, $X \in H$, $Z \in H^\perp$, and Y is a solution, then necessarily X is a solution; i.e., if (B.1b) is solvable, then there is one and only one solution X in the subspace H generated by $\{A_n\}_{n=1}^\infty$. The solution X is called an extremal solution and can be characterized in another manner. If K denotes the set of all Y contained in $\mathcal{H}$ such that Y solves (B.1b), then K is a closed convex subset of $\mathcal{H}$. Hence, there exists uniquely in K an element X such that $\|X\| < \|Y\|$ for $Y \in K$ and $Y \neq X$. The element X is obviously the extremal solution.

To study the solvability of (B.1b) we shall use some ideas from the theory of sequential weak convergence. Recall that if $Y_n \in \mathcal{H}$, then $\{Y_n\}_{n=1}^\infty$ is sequentially weakly convergent if and only if $\lim_n (Z, Y_n)$ exists for each $Z \in \mathscr{H}$. If H is a subspace of $\mathscr{H}$ and $Y_n \in H$, then a necessary and sufficient condition in order that $\{Y_n\}_{n=1}^{\infty}$ be sequentially weakly convergent is that (a) there exists $N > 0$ such that $\|Y_n\| \le N$, $n = 1, 2, \ldots$, and (b) there exists a dense subset K of H such that $\lim_n (A, Y_n)$ exists for each $A \in K$. These assertions follow readily from the diagonalization process.

Returning now to (B.1b), suppose (a) the set $\{A_n\}_{n=1}^{\infty}$ is linearly independent, (b) H_n denotes the subspace of $\mathscr{H}$ generated by $\{A_p\}_{p=1}^{n}$, $n = 1, 2, \ldots$, and (c) H denotes the subspace of $\mathscr{H}$ generated by $\{A_n\}_{n=1}^{\infty}$. Assumption (a) constitutes no loss of generality and is vital. It is equivalent to saying that the Grammian determinant

$$G_n = \begin{vmatrix} (A_1, A_1) & \cdots & (A_n, A_1) \\ \vdots & & \vdots \\ (A_1, A_n) & \cdots & (A_n, A_n) \end{vmatrix}$$

does not vanish for $n = 1, 2, \ldots$ (in fact, $G_n > 0$). In place of (B.1b) consider

$$(A_p, X^*) = \beta_p, \qquad p = 1, \ldots, n. \tag{B.1c}$$

If (B.1c) has a solution, then the extremal solution Y_n is the unique solution belonging to H_n and has the form

$$Y_n = \sum_{p=1}^{n} \alpha_p A_p.$$

Substituting this in (B.1c), we have

$$\bar{\beta}_j = (Y_n, A_j) = \sum_{p=1}^{\infty} \alpha_p (A_p, A_j), \qquad j = 1, \ldots, n,$$

and we can use Cramer's rule to solve for the α_j, thus showing that the solutions exist and leading to the following explicit expression for Y_n:

$$Y_n = G_n^{-1} \begin{vmatrix} (A_1, A_1) & \cdots & (A_n, A_1) & -\bar{\beta}_1 \\ \vdots & & \vdots & \vdots \\ (A_1, A_n) & \cdots & (A_n, A_n) & -\bar{\beta}_n \\ A_1 & \cdots & A_n & 0 \end{vmatrix}.$$

This gives us

$$\|Y_n\|^2 = (Y_n, Y_n) = G_n^{-1} \begin{vmatrix} (A_1, A_1) & \cdots & (A_n, A_1) & -\bar{\beta}_1 \\ \vdots & & \vdots & \vdots \\ (A_1, A_n) & \cdots & (A, A_n) & -\bar{\beta}_n \\ \beta_1 & \cdots & \beta_n & 0 \end{vmatrix}.$$

The last determinant is denoted by G'_n and $G'_n \geq 0$. In view of our comments on sequential weak convergence, we see that a sufficient condition for (B.1b) to have a solution is that

$$\sup_n G_n^{-1} G'_n < \infty. \tag{B.1d}$$

In view of our remarks concerning the extremal solution,

$$G_n^{-1} G'_n \leq G_{n+1}^{-1} G'_{n+1},$$

and this last inequality is valid for all n inasmuch as (B.1c) is solvable for all n.

Conversely, if (B.1b) is solvable and X is the extremal solution, then $X = Y_n + Y'_n$, $Y_n \in H_n$, $Y'_n \in H - H_n$ and $\|Y'_n\| \to 0$ as $n \to \infty$. Hence (B.1d) is also necessary.

For further details see [81] or [73]. Our presentation is taken from [73].

Appendix C

THE MOMENT PROBLEM

SUPPOSE $\{a_p\}_{p=0}^{\infty}$ IS a sequence and consider the infinite system of equations

$$a_p = \int_0^1 t^p \, d\varphi(t), \qquad p = 0,1,\ldots. \tag{C.1a}$$

The moment problem consists of determining conditions under which the above system can be solved for a normalized function φ of bounded variation on $[0,1]$. To formulate conditions for solvability, we set

$$\Delta^k a_p = \sum_{j=0}^{k} (-1)^j \binom{k}{j} a_{p+j}, \qquad p,k = 0,1,\ldots.$$

The basic theorem is that (C.1a) is solvable if and only if there exists $M > 0$ such that

$$\sum_{p=0}^{n} \binom{n}{p} |\Delta^{n-p} a_p| \le M, \qquad n = 0,1,\ldots. \tag{C.1b}$$

In view of Corollary 1.15.1 and the Riesz representation theorem for $C[0,1]$, whenever (C.1b) has a solution, the solution is necessarily unique.

We shall see that the condition (C.1b) is necessary. Without loss of generality we may assume φ is nondecreasing. Hence

$$0 \le \Delta^{n-p} a_p = \int_0^1 (1 - t)^{n-p} t^p \, d\varphi(t)$$

and

$$\sum_{p=0}^{n} \binom{n}{p} \Delta^{n-p} a_p = \int_0^1 \sum_{p=0}^{n} (1 - t)^{n-p} t^p \, d\varphi(t) = \int_0^1 d\varphi(t) = \varphi(1).$$

148

Inasmuch as the central theme of this monograph is approximation theory, we shall prove the sufficiency by using the Bernstein polynomials. If $f \in C[0,1]$, then the nth Bernstein polynomial of f is defined by

$$B_n(f,t) = \sum_{p=0}^{n} \binom{n}{p}(1 - t)^{n-p}t^p f\left(\frac{p}{n}\right).$$

The Bernstein polynomial theorem asserts that $B_n(f,t)$ converges uniformly to $f(t)$ on $[0,1]$. In virtue of Corollary 1.15.1 we can establish the last assertion by showing its validity for the functions $f_m(t) = t^m$, $m = 0,1,\ldots$. To this end,

$$f_0(t) \equiv 1 \equiv ([1 - t] + t)^n = \sum_{p=0}^{n} \binom{n}{p}(1 - t)^{n-p}t^p \equiv B_n(f_0,t).$$

On differentiating the last expression and multiplying by t, we get

$$t \equiv \sum_{p=0}^{n} \binom{n}{p}(1 - t)^{n-p}t^p \frac{p}{n} \equiv B_n(f_1,t).$$

Continuing this process we get $B_n(f_2,t) = t^2 + n^{-1}t$ or, in general, $B_n(f_m,t) = a_n t^m + P_n(t)$, where $a_n \to 1$ and $\|P_n\| \to 0$ as $n \to \infty$.

Suppose now that we are given a sequence $\{a_p\}_{p=0}^{\infty}$ satisfying (C.1b). We define a linear function L on the vector space of polynomials contained in $C[0,1]$ such that

$$\alpha a_p + \beta a_q = L(\alpha t^p + \beta t^q).$$

Equation (C.1b) implies that L can be extended to an element of $C^*[0,1]$. In fact, for $f \in C[0,1]$,

$$|L(B_n(f,t))| = \left| \sum_{p=0}^{n} \binom{n}{p} \Delta^{n-p}a_p f\left(\frac{p}{n}\right) \right| \le M \cdot \|f\|.$$

Hence, for $f \in C[0,1]$, we define $T(f) = \lim_{n \to \infty} L(B_n(f,t))$. To complete this argument we need to show that

$$\lim_n L(B_n(f_m,t)) = a_m,$$

$f_m(t) = t^m$, $m = 0,1,\ldots$. To this end, if $n > m \ge 1$, then

$$a_m - L(B_n(f_m,t)) = \sum_{p=m}^{n} \left\{ \frac{p(p - 1)\cdots(p - m + 1)}{n(n - 1)\cdots(n - m + 1)} - \left(\frac{p}{n}\right)^m \right\} (\Delta^{n-1}a_p)\binom{n}{p}$$

$$- \sum_{p=0}^{m-1} \binom{n}{p}(\Delta^{n-p}a_p)\left(\frac{p}{n}\right)^m.$$

Setting $t_p = n^{-1}p$, the first term on the right becomes

$$\sum_{p=m}^{n} \left\{ \frac{p(p-1)\cdots(p-m+1)}{n(n-1)\cdots(n-m+1)} - t_p^m \right\} (\Delta^{n-p}a_p)\binom{n}{p}. \qquad \text{(C.1c)}$$

Since m is fixed, we have for $\varepsilon > 0$ that there exists $n_0 > n$ such that $n > n_0$ implies

$$\left| \frac{nt(nt-1)\cdots(nt-m+1)}{n(n-1)\cdots(n-m+1)} - t^n \right| < t$$

uniformly in $t \in [0,1]$. Consequently, (C.1c) is dominated by

$$\varepsilon \sum_{p=m}^{n} \binom{n}{p} |\Delta^{n-p}a_p| \le \varepsilon M.$$

Finally, there exists $n_1 > 0$ such that $n > n_1$ implies

$$\left| \sum_{p=0}^{m-1} \binom{n}{p}(\Delta^{n-p}a_p)\left(\frac{p}{n}\right)^m \right| \le \left(\frac{m-1}{n}\right) \sum_{p=0}^{m-1} \binom{n}{p}|\Delta^{n-p}a_p| < \varepsilon M.$$

Suppose that φ is a nondecreasing function on $[0,2\pi]$ and

$$a_p = \int_0^{2\pi} (\sin^2 t/2)^p \, d\varphi(t) \qquad p = 0,1,\ldots; \qquad \text{(C.1d)}$$

then

$$\sum_{p=0}^{n} \binom{n}{p}|\Delta^{n-p}a_p| = \int_0^{2\pi} (\cos t/2)^{2(n-p)}(\sin t/2)^{2p} \, d\varphi(t) = \varphi(2\pi).$$

Hence, the sequence $\{a_p\}_{p=0}^{\infty}$ is a moment sequence. We used this in the proof of Theorem 2.3.

Our presentation is taken from [92]. For additional details concerning Bernstein polynomials see [47].

REFERENCES

[1] R. D. Anderson, "A characterization of the universal curve and a proof of its homogenity," *Ann. Math.*, **67**, 313–324 (1958).

[2] S. Banach, *Théorie des opérations linéaires*, Monografje Matematyezne, Warsaw, Poland, 1932.

[3] W. Blaschke, "Eine Erweiterung des Satzes von Vitali uber Folgen analytischer Funktionen," *Leipzig Ber.*, **67**, 194–209 (1915).

[4] S. Bochner, "Boundary values of analytic functions in several variables and almost periodic functions," *Ann. Math.*, **45**, 708–722 (1944).

[5] S. Bochner, *Vorlesungen über Fouriersche Integrale*, Akademic Verlag, Liepzig, 1932.

[6] H. F. Bohenblust and A. Sobczyk, "Extensions of functionals on complex linear spaces," *Bull. Am. Math. Soc.*, **44**, 91–93 (1938).

[7] H. Bremekamp, "Uber die Carsonsche Integralgleichung," *Koninkl. Akad. Nsd. Wetenschap., Proc. (Sciences)*, **40**, 689–694 (1937).

[8] R. M. Brooks, "A ring of analytic functions," *Studia Math.*, **24**, 191–210 (1964).

[9] R. C. Buck, "Bounded continuous functions on a locally compact space," *Mich. Math. J.*, **5**, 95–104 (1958).

[10] A. Buerling, "On two problems concerning linear transformations in Hilbert space," *Acta Math.*, **81**, 239–255 (1949).

[11] A. P. Calderon, "On theorems of M. Riesz and Zygmund," *Proc. Am. Math. Soc.*, **1**, 533–535 (1950).

[12] C. Caratheodory, *Theory of Functions, Vol. II*, Chelsea, New York, 1960.

[13] J. B. Conway, Thesis, Louisiana State University, Baton Rouge, La., 1965.

[14] R. Courant, "Über eine Eigenschaft der Abbildungs-funktionen bei Konformen abbeildung," *Gott. Nachr., Math. Phys. Kl.*, **1914**, 101–109; **1929**, 67–70.

[15] R. G. Crownoner, "Concerning a function algebra," *Studia Math.*, **25** (1965).

[16] P. J. Davis, *Interpolation and Approximation*, Blaisdell, New York, 1963.

[17] M. M. Day, "The space L^p with $0 < p < 1$," *Bull. Am. Math. Soc.*, **46**, 816–823 (1940).

[18] K. deLeeuw and W. Rudin, "Extreme points and extremum problems in H_1," *Pacific J. Math.*, **8**, 467–485 (1958).

[19] R. G. Douglas, Thesis, Louisiana State University, Baton Rouge, La., 1962.

[20] N. Dunford and J. T. Schwartz, *"Linear Operators, Part I,"* Wiley—Interscience, New York, 1958.

[21] G. Fichera, "On completeness of sequences of reciprocals of linear functions," *M.R.C. Tech. Rept. 117*, **1959**, Madison, Wis.

[22] O. Frostman, "Potentiel d'équilibre et capacité des ensembles," *Lund Univ. Math. Seminar*, **3** (1935).

[23] L. Gillman and M. Jerison, *Rings of Continuous Functions*, Van Nostrand, Princeton, N.J., 1960.

[24] G. H. Hardy, "An inequality between integrals," *Mess. Math.*, **51**, 186–192 (1922).

[25] G. H. Hardy, "On the mean value of the modulus of an analytic function," *Proc. London Math. Soc.* (Ser. 2), **14**, 269–277 (1915).

[26] F. Hartogs and A. Rosenthal, "Über Folgen analytischer Funktionen," *Math. Ann.*, **100**, 218–263 (1928).

[27] W. K. Hayman, *Lectures on Meromorphic Functions*, Tata Institute, Bombay, 1959.

[28] W. K. Hayman, *Meromorphic Functions*, Oxford Univ. Press, New York, 1964.

[29] W. K. Hayman, "On Nevanlinna's second theorem and extension," *Rend. Mat. Palermo* (Ser. 2), **2**, 346–391 (1953).

[30] H. Helson, *Lectures on Invariant Subspaces*, Academic Press, New York, 1964.

[31] H. Helson and D. Lowdenslager, "Prediction theory and Fourier series in several variables," *Acta Math.*, **99**, 165–202 (1958).

[32] E. Hewitt, "The ranges of certain convolution operators," *Math. Scand.*, **15**, 147–155 (1964).

[33] D. Hilbert, *Grundzüge einer allgemeinen Theorie der linearen Integralgleichungen*, Teubner, Leipzig, 1912.

[34] E. Hille, *Analytic Function Theory*, Ginn, Boston, 1962.

[35] E. Hille and R. S. Phillips, "Functional analysis and semigroups," *Colloq. Publ. Am. Math. Soc.*, Vol. 31, Providence, R. I., 1957.

[36] J. G. Hocking and G. S. Young, *Topology*, Addison–Wesley, Reading, Mass., 1961.

[37] K. Hoffman, *Banach Spaces of Analytic Functions*, Prentice-Hall, Englewood Cliffs, N.J., 1962.

[38] W. Hurewicz and H. Wallman, *Dimension Theory*, Princeton Univ. Press, Princeton, N. J., 1941.

[39] A. Hurwitz, "Über die Nullstellen der Bessel'chen Funktion," *Math. Ann.*, **33**, 211–218 (1889).

[40] S. Kakutani, "Concrete representation of abstract M spaces," *Ann. Math.*, **42**, 934–1024 (1941).

[41] M. Krein and D. Milman, "On extreme points of regularly convex sets," *Studia Math.*, **9**, 133–138 (1940).

[42] M. Lavrentieff, *Sur les fonctions d'une variable complexe representables par des series de polynomes*, Act. Sci. Ind., Paris, 1936.

[43] K. O. Leland, "A polynomial approach to topological analysis," prepublication manuscript.

[44] K. O. Leland, Thesis, Louisiana State University, Baton Rouge, La., 1963.

[45] A. E. Livingston, "The space H^p, $0 < p < 1$, is not normable," *Pacific J. Math.*, **3**, 613–616 (1953).

[46] L. H. Loomis, *An Introduction to Abstract Harmonic Analysis*, Van Nostrand, Princeton, N. J., 1953.

[47] G. G. Lorentz, *Bernstein Polynomials*, Toronto, 1953.

[48] J. Malmquist, "Étude d'une fonction entière," *Acta. Math.* (*Uppsala*), **29**, 203–215 (1905).

[49] A. J. Maria, "The potential of a positive mass and the weight function of Wiener," *Proc. Natl. Acad. Sci. U.S.*, **20**, 485–489 (1934).

[50] P. Masani and N. Wiener, "The prediction theory of multivariate stochastic processes, II," *Acta Math.*, **99**, 93–137 (1958).

[51] S. N. Mergelyan, "Certain classes of sets and their applications" (translation), *Soviet Math.*, **2**, 590–593 (1961).

[52] P. Montel, *Leçons sur les familles normales de fonctions analytiques et leurs applications*, Gauthier–Villars, Paris, 1927.

[53] P. Montel, *Leçons sur les series de polynomes à une variable complexe*, Gauthier–Villars, Paris, 1910.

[54] M. C. Mooney, Thesis, Louisiana State University, Baton Rouge, La., 1965.

[55] R. L. Moore, "Foundations of point set theory," *Colloq. Publ. Am. Math. Soc.*, Vol. 13, Providence, R. I., 1962 (revised edition).

[56] J. Moser and P. Porcelli, "Note on the completeness of Hermite functions," *M.R.C. Tech. Rept. 107*, Madison, Wis.

[57] C. H. Muntz, *Über den Approximationssatz von Weierstrass*, Schwarz's Festschrift, Berlin, 1914, pp. 303–1312.

[58] M. A. Naimark, *Normed Rings* (rev. ed.), Nordhoff, Groningen, 1964.

[59] R. Nevanlinna, *Eindeutige analytische Funktionen*, Springer, Berlin, 1936.

[60] A. Ostrowski, "Mathematische Miszellen III," *Jahresber Deut. Math.*, **34**, 161–171 (1925).

[61] R. E. A. C. Paley, "On the lacumary coefficients of a power series," *Ann. Math.*, **34**, 615–616 (1933).

[62] R. E. A. C. Paley and N. Wiener, "Fourier transforms in the complex domain," *Colloq. Publ. Am. Math. Soc.*, Vol. 14, Providence, R.I., 1934.

[63] G. Polya and G. Szegö, *Aufgaben und Lehrsätze aus der analysis*, Vol. II, Springer, Berlin, 1925.

[64] P. Porcelli, (1) Ajoint spaces of abstract L_p spaces, and (2) Closure properties of Hilbert–Stieltjes kernels, Notes (Math. Dept.), Louisiana State University, Baton Rouge, La.

[65] P. Porcelli, "Interpolation and approximation with rational functions," *J. Louisiana Acad. Sci.*, **27**, 118–125 (1964).

[66] P. Porcelli, "Note on a Stieltjes type of inversion," *Can. J. Math.*, **8**, 446–447 (1956).

[67] P. Porcelli, "On the distribution of zeros of successive derivatives of bounded analytic functions," *Rend. Mat.*, **20**, 385–394 (1961).

[68] P. Porcelli, "Representation of derivatives of analytic functions by a multi-dimensional type of LaPlace transform," *J. Louisiana Acad. Sci.*, **27**, 110–113 (1964).

[69] P. Porcelli, "Uniform completeness of sets of reciprocals of linear functions," *Duke Math. J.*, **20**, 185–193 (1953).

[70] P. Porcelli, "Uniform completeness of sets of reciprocals of linear functions, II," *Duke Math. J.*, **21**, 595–598 (1954).

[71] D. Raikov, "Positive definite functions on commutative groups with invariant measure" (in Russian), *Dokl. Akad.*, **28**, 296–300 (1940).

[72] C. E. Rickart, *General Theory of Branch Algebras*, Van Nostrand, Princeton, N.J., 1960.

[73] F. Riesz, *Les Systemes d'équations linéaires à une infinité d'inconnues*, Gauthier–Villars, Paris, 1913.

[74] F. Riesz, "Sur certains systèmes singuliers d'équations integrales," *Ann. École Norm. Sup.*, **28**, 33–62 (1911).

[75] F. Riesz, "Über die randwerte analytischer Funktionen," *Math. Z.*, **18**, 87–95 (1923).

[76] M. Riesz, "Sur les fonctions conjuguies," *Math. Z.*, **27**, 218–244 (1927).

[77] F. and M. Riesz, "Über die randwerte analytischer Funktionen," *Scand. Math. Congr.*, Stockholm, 1916.

[78] W. Rudin, *Fourier Analysis on Groups*, Wiley–Interscience, New York, 1962.

[79] W. Rudin, "Factorization in the group algebra of the real line," *Proc. Natl. Acad. Sci. U.S.*, **43**, 339–340 (1957).

[80] C. Runge, "Zur theorie der eindeutigen analytischen Funktionen," *Acta Math.*, **6**, 229–244 (1885).

[81] E. Schmidt, "Über die auflösung linearer Gleichungen mit Abzählbar unendlichen vielen unbekannten," *Rend. Circ. Mat. Palermo*, **25**, 53–77 (1908).

[82] A. Shields and L. Rubel, "Weak topologies on the bounded holomorphic functions," *Bull. Am. Math. Soc.*, **71**, 349, 352 (1965).

[83] M. H. Stone, "The generalized Weierstrass approximation theorem," *Math. Mag.*, **21**, 167–184, 237–254 (1948).

[84] G. Szegö, "Über dichte Funktionenfamilien," *Ber. Verhandl. Kgl., Sachsischen Ges. Wiss. Leipzig, Math.-Phys. Kl.*, **78**, 373–380 (1926).

[85] O. Szasz, "Über die approximation stetiger Funktionen durch gegebene Funktionenfolgen," *Math. Ann.*, **104**, 155–160 (1930–1931).

[86] O. Szasz, "Über die approximation stetiger Funktionen durch lineare aggregate von Potenzen," *Math. Ann.*, **77**, 482–496 (1916).

[87] A. E. Taylor, *Introduction to Functional Analysis*, Wiley–Interscience, New York, 1958.

[88] E. C. Titchmarch, *Introduction to the Theory of Fourier Integrals*, Oxford Univ. Press, New York, 1937.

[89] E. C. Titchmarsh, *The Theory of Functions*, Oxford Univ. Press, New York, 1952.

[90] M. Tsuji, *Potential Theory in Modern Function Theory*, Tokyo, 1959.

[91] C. G. G. van Herk, "A class of completely monotonic functions," *Comp. Math.*, **9**, 1–79 (1951).

[92] H. S. Wall, *Analytic Theory of Continued Fractions*, New York, 1948.

[93] J. L. Walsh, "Interpolation and approximation," *Colloq. Publ., Am. Math. Soc.*, Vol. 20, Providence, R.I., 1935.

[94] S. S. Walters, "Remarks on the space H^p," *Pacific J. Math.*, **1**, 455–471 (1951).

[95] S. S. Walters, "The space H^p with $0 < p < 1$," *Proc. Am. Math. Soc.*, **1**, 800–805 (1950).

[96] G. T. Whyburn, *Topological Analysis*, Princeton, N.J., 1964.

[97] D. V. Widder, *The LaPlace Transform*, Princeton, N.J., 1946.

[98] A. Zygmund, *Trigonometric Series*, 2nd ed., Vols. I and II, Cambridge Univ. Press, New York, 1959.

INDEX

DATE DUE

OC 8 '67			
GAYLORD			PRINTED IN U.S A.